PRAIRIE CHICKENS OF KANSAS

BY

MAURICE F. BAKER

STATE BIOLOGICAL SURVEY

UNIVERSITY OF KANSAS

LAWRENCE · KANSAS

UNIVERSITY OF KANSAS

MUSEUM OF NATURAL HISTORY
AND
STATE BIOLOGICAL SURVEY OF KANSAS

EDITOR: E. RAYMOND HALL

Miscellaneous Publication No. 5, pp. 1-68, plates 1-4, figures 1-15,

Published March 10, 1953

PRINTED BY
FERD VOILAND, JR., STATE PRINTER
TOPEKA, KANSAS
1953

24-6795

TABLE OF CONTENTS

	PAGE
INTRODUCTION	4
THE LESSER PRAIRIE CHICKEN	7
THE GREATER PRAIRIE CHICKEN	9
History	9
Characteristics of the Range and Present Distribution	12
LIFE HISTORY OF THE GREATER PRAIRIE CHICKEN	17
General Remarks	17
Description of the Welda Area	18
Daily Routine of One Flock	19
Activities of Males on the Booming Ground	22
Summer Activities of Males	23
Reproductive Cycle of Females	23
Nesting	24
Rate of Egg Laying	25
Period of Incubation	26
Success of Nests	26
Size of Clutch	27
Decline in Size of Broods	29
PLUMAGES OF THE GREATER PRAIRIE CHICKEN	31
Development of Plumage in the Young	31
Age Based on the Condition of the Molt	36
Molt of the Adult Greater Prairie Chicken	38
Length of Primaries as Correlated with Age and Sex	39
WEIGHTS OF THE GREATER PRAIRIE CHICKEN IN AUTUMN	41
FOOD HABITS OF THE GREATER PRAIRIE CHICKEN	43
POPULATION CHANGES OF THE GREATER PRAIRIE CHICKEN	51
The 1949-1952 Decline in Numbers	53
Changes in Age Composition	56
Changes in Sex Composition	57
Differences in Abundance as Indicated by Hunters' Success	57
MANAGEMENT	59
Census	59
Hunting Regulations and Refuges	61
Range and Pasture Management	62
Restocking	64
SUMMARY AND RECOMMENDATIONS	64
LITERATURE CITED	66

PRAIRIE CHICKENS OF KANSAS

INTRODUCTION

THE GREATER prairie chicken is a two-pound gallinaceous bird, of the grouse family (Tetraonidae), formerly common but now rare or absent from many parts of its former range. Kansas, fortunately, still has extensive areas suitable for this bird, and is one of the four states having the largest number of the greater prairie chicken. The Dakotas and Nebraska are the other states. This bird is popular with hunters; other persons also take pride in the fact that sizeable flocks persist in parts of the State. But, what caused the bird to disappear in many areas when it remained in others? Can it be preserved? Can it be managed so that a part of the annual increase can be harvested as game, at intervals, without depleting the breeding stock? These and other questions had occurred to many Kansans. At the University of Kansas, graduate students Lester Lew Henry and the late Wilbur S. Long had gathered considerable information concerning this game bird. Naturally, therefore, the greater prairie chicken was chosen for one of the initial studies when the State Biological Survey of Kansas was reactivated in 1949.

Actually there are two species of prairie chickens and both occur, even today, in Kansas. The lesser prairie chicken, *Tympanuchus pallidicinctus* (Ridgway), lives in the southwestern prairies (see Figure 1). It is so uniform in size, color and bodily proportions throughout its range that no geographic populations are recognized as separate subspecies.

The greater prairie chicken, *Tympanuchus cupido* (Linnaeus), occurs to the eastward of the other species (see Figure 1). Three geographic variants (subspecies) are recognized. The first of these is the heath hen, *T. c. cupido* (Linnaeus), that formerly occurred in the northern Atlantic States, but that now is extinct. The last bird of this subspecies died in 1931, and an account of the unsuccessful efforts to save the subspecies is given by Gross (1928).

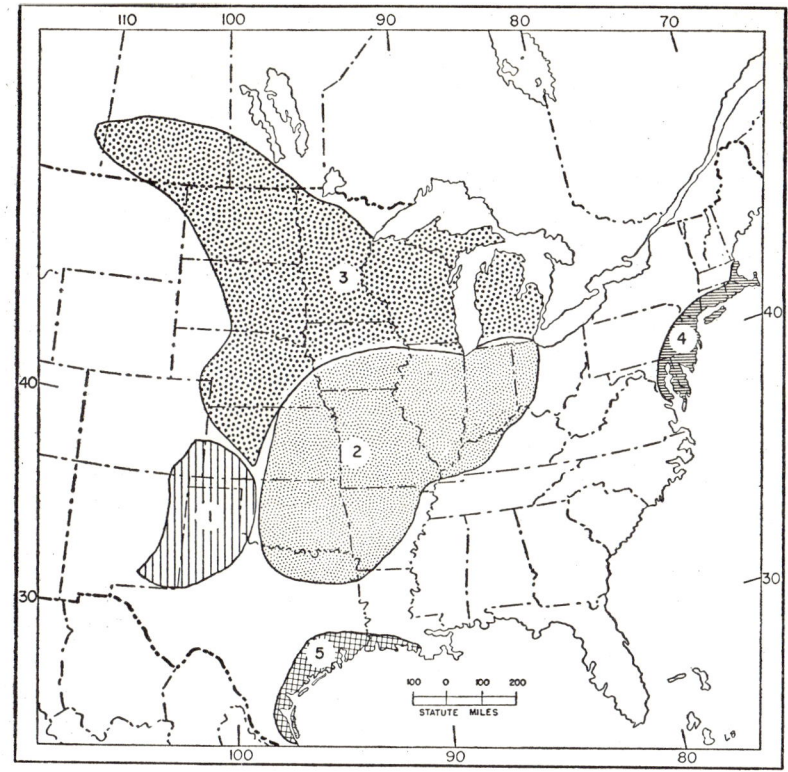

FIG. 1. Geographic distribution of the genus *Tympanuchus* Gloger. (1) Range of *T. pallidicinctus* (Ridgway); (2) original range of *T. c. pinnatus* (Brewster); (3) range occupied by *T. c. pinnatus* since cultivated crops were introduced; (4) former range of *T. c. cupido* (Linnaeus), now extinct; (5) range of *T. c. attwateri* Bendire. *T. c. pinnatus* now absent in much of its former range.

The second subspecies is the Attwater prairie chicken, *T. c. attwateri* Bendire, which inhabits the prairies of the Gulf Coast of Texas. It still persists in a few places, and an account of its natural history is given by Lehmann (1941). The third subspecies is commonly known as the greater prairie chicken, *T. c. pinnatus* (Brewster); it occurs in the grasslands of the Midwest.

Before the Midwest was settled the greater prairie chicken lived in the Tall-grass Prairies of the eastern and southern parts of what is now the United States. With the development of primitive agriculture, it extended its range to the west and to the north as far as parts of the Prairie Provinces of Canada. As stated by Ridgway and Friedmann (1946:207), the range of the genus, originally and since the arrival of the white man, is "Open districts of eastern North America, from the western . . . Great Plains to the Atlantic coast (locally) and from Texas and southwestern Louisiana (formerly also Virginia?) northward to coast of Massachusetts, southwestern Ontario, southern Manitoba, and southwestern Saskatchewan."

Ecologically, Kansas, with which we are immediately concerned, is an area of transition from the eastern hardwood forest to the western mixed prairie. Primitively, the diverse conditions in this transitional area provided suitable habitat for: the wild turkey, *Meleagris gallopavo* Linnaeus; the ruffed grouse, *Bonasa umbellus* (Linnaeus); the sharp-tailed grouse, *Pedioecetes phasianellus* (Linnaeus); the bobwhite quail, *Colinus virginianus* (Linnaeus); the scaled quail, *Callipepla squamata* (Vigors); the lesser prairie chicken; and the greater prairie chicken. Without exception each of these birds, in Kansas, was at the periphery of its range. As Kansas was occupied and developed by white men from the eastern states, the turkey, the ruffed grouse and the sharp-tailed grouse became extinct in the State, and the ranges and numbers of the two prairie chickens were reduced. Recently residents of Rawlins and Cheyenne counties have reported that the sharp-tailed grouse is spreading from Nebraska into extreme northwestern Kansas (field notes on file in Univ. Kansas Museum of Nat. Hist., for 31 October 1952, and 2 November 1952, P. H. Baker). Although man has introduced the ring-necked pheasant, *Phasianus colchicus* Linnaeus, to compensate partly for this loss, the fauna of gallinaceous birds in Kansas is poorer by one species; this loss, at least in part, is the result of the activities of man.

The aims of this study were to ascertain the present status of the prairie chickens in Kansas, and to learn previously unknown details of their life histories, habits and population behavior. Such information would be expected to aid in the conservation of the two species of birds. The investigation was concerned primarily with the greater prairie chicken, but such information as was obtained on the lesser prairie chicken is included.

The co-operation and assistance rendered me by residents of the Welda Area where intensive field studies were made are gratefully acknowledged. Mr. William Brecheisen, Jr., was especially helpful. Also I thank the employees of the Kansas Forestry, Fish and Game Commission, especially Mr. Dave Leahy, Director, for the assistance rendered in ascertaining the ranges of the two species of prairie chickens. These employees as well as several graduate students and faculty members at the University of Kansas gathered essential data on the numbers of the greater prairie chicken killed in the open seasons of 1950, 1951 and 1952. There at the University Mrs. Louise Brunk gave assistance with the line drawings. The drawings made by Mr. Richard Philip Grossenheider and Mr. Victor Hogg are identifiable by their signatures. Photographs are by the author, except as otherwise noted. Dr. Harrison B. Tordoff gave assistance in the study of the molt in the young of the greater prairie chicken, and Dr. Rollin H. Baker gave helpful criticisms, suggestions and encouragement throughout the course of the research. Both he and Dr. E. Raymond Hall gave critical assistance with the preparation of the manuscript.

THE LESSER PRAIRIE CHICKEN

The writers of many accounts concerning prairie chickens in Kansas do not differentiate between the two species. Therefore, and because the lesser prairie chicken was not recognized as a distinct species until 1885, it is difficult to determine the early status of the lesser prairie chicken. Probably the chief breeding range of the lesser prairie chicken in Kansas always has been confined to the southwestern counties. According to Duck and Fletcher (1945?:68), some early settlers in western Oklahoma recognized two kinds of prairie chickens in the same area, but occurring on different mating grounds. The "booming and cooing kind" (greater prairie chicken) was found in the uplands, and the "gobbling kind" (lesser prairie chicken) was found in the sandhills along water courses. If the former breeding range as mapped by Duck and Fletcher (*op. cit.*, Map II) in Oklahoma be extended into Kansas on the basis of similar soils, the former range would have extended as far east as the western part of Harper County, Kansas.

In Kansas, the lesser prairie chicken has been taken as far east as Anderson and Neosho counties. The records from Neosho County are of a male and a female taken by Goss (see Goss, 1891:221) near Chanute on December 31, 1878, and on January 17, 1879, respectively. I have examined these mounted specimens and the original catalogue of Goss in the Kansas Historical Museum, Topeka, Kansas, and there is no doubt that these specimens are lesser prairie chickens. These records are incorrectly cited by

Ridgway and Friedmann (1946:221) as from Neosho Falls, which was Goss' home.

Other eastern records are as follows: A specimen in the Hurter Collection from southwestern Missouri, no date (Bent, 1932:285); a specimen in the collection of the Academy of Natural Sciences of Philadelphia from Garnett (spelled Garneth in Bent), Kansas, January 24-28, 1894 (Bent, *loc. cit.*); a male from Greenwood County, Kansas, in the "Rinker Collection," July or August 1895 (Long, 1937:78). Probably it is significant that none of these specimens, for which the date of collection is given, was taken in the breeding season. The University of Kansas Museum of Natural History has only one specimen from outside the present breeding range of the species and that is from Logan County; the bird was taken on January 1, 1921. Game Protector E. L. Bryan reported to me (*in litt.*, June 13, 1950) that the lesser prairie chicken formerly occurred in Trego, Ellis and Graham counties, Kansas. Probably this species formerly bred as far north as the counties just mentioned, even though the greater prairie chicken also bred there.

No evidence has been found that the lesser prairie chicken ever was reduced greatly in numbers in Kansas until the dry years of the 1930-1940 decade. Immediately prior to that time the species was abundant. According to the statement of a resident of Meade County, Kansas, the people of that area depended upon the lesser prairie chicken for food in place of domestic poultry, and the birds were taken whenever needed. In approximately 1928, three men shot 107 lesser prairie chickens on one morning, before 8 A. M., south of Garden City in Finney County.

The drought of the 1930-1940 decade seems to have almost eliminated the lesser prairie chicken in Kansas. Little food, cover or water was available over large areas, and numbers of lesser prairie chickens were reported to have been found dead with their nostrils clogged with dust. Edward Gebhard, of Meade, thinks that the only lesser prairie chickens left in Kansas at the end of the drought were on the XI Ranch, approximately 75 square miles, in Meade County, and a few on the Hitch Ranch in Seward County. "Buck" Adams of the XI Ranch reported that lesser prairie chickens came to the ranch headquarters for water in the drought years, and that only one small flock survived on the entire ranch.

In 1950, the game protectors of the Kansas Forestry, Fish and Game Commission were questioned by mail to learn in which of the 105 counties prairie chickens were present. They were reported in 57 of the counties. Subsequent field investigation disclosed that the prairie chickens in the 14 southwestern counties were lesser prairie chickens, and that they were confined to the sandy lands that lie south of the Arkansas and Cimarron rivers (see Figure 2).

The residents of southwestern Kansas report that these sandy lands supported stands of tall grasses before the drought of the 1930-1940 decade. These grasses were eliminated over wide areas in the drought, and were replaced by sagebrush, *Artemisia* sp.; to date the grasses have not completely recovered. In ungrazed areas, tall grasses are crowding out the sagebrush, but in thousands of acres of rangeland, the sagebrush and short grasses predominate. Unless the native grasses effect a considerable recovery, the lesser prairie chicken may not approach its former abundance.

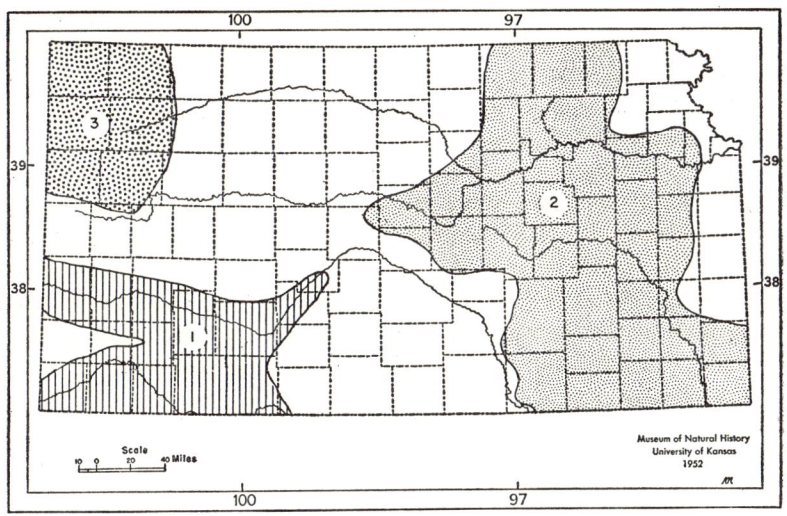

Fig. 2. The geographic distribution of prairie chickens in Kansas. (1) Range of the lesser prairie chicken; (2) the chief range of the greater prairie chicken; (3) range wherein scattered flocks of the greater prairie chicken were reported present in 1950.

A count of lesser prairie chickens on booming grounds on four and one-half square miles of some of the best range on the XI Ranch in the spring of 1951 revealed a total of 40 males on five booming grounds. A count on the same area in the spring of 1952 revealed 82 males. This increase in numbers is encouraging, but the limited range suitable for the lesser prairie chicken in Kansas should be considered in any plans for its management.

The Greater Prairie Chicken

History

The distribution and abundance of this species in Kansas before the State was settled by white men, can only be inferred from the

[9]

accounts of early explorers. It seems that the greater prairie chicken did not occur farther west than the middle of Kansas, and that the bird did not occur in impressively large numbers. The second point may be inferred from the lack of comment concerning the species by early explorers. Pike (see Coues, 1895:357-459) never mentioned seeing prairie chickens in his travels across Kansas in the autumn of 1806. Tixier (see McDermott, 1940:102-131) in 1840 traveled overland from Independence, Missouri, to the Osage Village, thought to have been in Labette County, Kansas. He mentions seeing prairie chickens (presumably greater prairie chickens) twice in Missouri near settlements, but never records their presence in the Territory of Kansas. More significantly, part of his party subsisted for two days on four upland plovers, *Bartramia longicauda* (Bechstein), during an enforced stay on the prairie. Prairie chickens probably were scarce or absent; if they had been abundant they probably would have been used for food in place of the upland plovers. Of approximately 25 references to the "prairie hen" in Thwaites (1904-1906), none is certainly referable to the genus *Tympanuchus* except in settled areas. Most significantly, Koch (1836:163) mentions that the numbers of prairie chickens (presumably greater prairie chickens) increased within three years after settlement of the prairie lands, and suggests that the cause of the increase was the food made available by cultivation.

Baird (1860:628) wrote of the prairie chicken, "It scarcely seems to occur north of the United States line, nor, perhaps, beyond the beginning of the High Central Plains." McClanahan (1940:13) maps the western edge of the original range of this species in Kansas from approximately the eastern edge of Barber County, almost due north to the Nebraska-Kansas line. Duck and Fletcher (1945?:68), after analyzing early records in Oklahoma and after talking to old residents of that state, concluded that the greater prairie chicken occupied most of the state east of the Panhandle, and mapped the western boundary of its range as crossing the Kansas line south of Medicine Lodge. Thus, it seems that before the coming of the white man, the greater prairie chicken in Kansas was confined to the eastern half of the State.

Coincident with the development of intensive agriculture in the eastern part of the State, the numbers of greater prairie chickens declined in that area in the latter part of the 19th century. At the same time these birds occupied previously unused range in western Kansas, but later the center of population shifted back to the east. Goss (1891:225) says of this species, "common in the eastern and middle portion of the State and spreading westward with its settlement." Cooke (1900:202) reported that the greater prairie chicken first nested in Colorado in approximately 1899. Dyche (1912:10) reports, "In former years . . . prairie chickens were found in great numbers, especially in the eastern part. At present . . . prairie chickens are confined to counties in the western part of the State." Bunker (1913:146) states relative to the greater prairie chicken, "Formerly an abundant resident; still common in some parts of western Kansas." In the period 1912-1913, prairie chickens seemed to be at an all time low in Kansas; anyhow a few years later Clapp (1922:9) wrote: "Prairie chicken, one of the very finest game birds, and formerly abundant all over the State, was practically extinct ten years ago. This bird has come back handsomely and is now found in all sections where conditions are favorable, even in the extreme eastern counties of the State."

A parallel to this situation is described by Yeatter (1943:378) for Illinois. There, a general decline occurred from approximately 1880 until 1903 when the hunting season was closed for the first time. By 1912, prairie chickens again had become sufficiently numerous in some areas to elicit complaints from farmers. Thus, the lowest population level in Illinois and Kansas did not occur at the same time, but both declines may have resulted from local conditions such as reduction in suitable range and overshooting.

Since 1922, the greater prairie chicken has almost disappeared from northwestern Kansas, and has remained on a more or less stable range in parts of the eastern one-third of the State (see Figure 2). The record is not clear as to which species it was that Dyche (*loc. cit.*) and Clapp (*loc. cit.*) referred, but according to Long (1937:77) the remnant population in northwestern Kansas is of the greater prairie chicken. Specimens of the greater prairie chicken from western Kansas in the University of Kansas Museum of Natural History are, together with the year taken, from Ellis County, 1904; Rooks County, 1905; Trego County, 1906; Osborne County, 1907; Trego County, 1927.

From the foregoing record, it seems that the population and range of the greater prairie chicken have changed much in the past 100 years. Since the habitat requirements of a species would not be expected to change, the cause of such changes in occupied range must be sought in the habitat itself. Among possible causes of changes in habitat are changes in climate and land-use. Considering man as a part of the habitat, hunting pressure must also be considered as a contributing factor to these changes. Flora (1948:3-5) says that there has been no definite trend toward increase or decrease in amount of precipitation in Kansas, but that since approximately 1890 there has been a trend toward warmer weather. This trend could hardly be a factor in the extension of the range of the greater prairie chicken into northwestern Kansas, because this bird can winter successfully in colder areas (Canada).

In the biennial reports of the State Department of Agriculture, grain is mentioned as produced in Graham County as early as 1885 and in Wallace County as early as 1890. The increase of winter foods, available to the greater prairie chicken, that accompanied this farming might well explain this westward extension of the range of the bird. It is thought that the changes in food and cover, especially the reduction of the tall grasses, that accompanied the dry years of the 1930-1940 decade, almost eliminated the greater prairie chicken from northwestern Kansas.

The disappearance of the greater prairie chicken from much of eastern Kansas is attributable to the reduction of native grasslands by plowing and by the natural succession of woodlands after prairie fires were excluded. In areas where the greater prairie chicken now occurs in eastern Kansas, grasslands always have been at least as extensive as at present. The near elimination of the greater prairie chicken in eastern Kansas prior to 1913 may have resulted mostly from excessive hunting.

Characteristics of the Range and Present Distribution

Information received from game protectors in 1950 indicated that in four northwestern counties there were only scattered flocks of greater prairie chickens containing few birds. Greater prairie chickens in Washington, Clay, Ottawa, Saline, Ellsworth and McPherson counties also proved to be in widely scattered flocks using untilled parts of the Central Kansas Rolling Plains Region (see Fly, 1946:map). According to Fly (1946:163) much of this area is badly eroded. If needed soil conservation measures, including range—and pasture-improvement, were applied there, the area probably would become an important part of the range of the greater prairie chicken in Kansas.

With the assistance of the local game protectors and other persons the principal range of the greater prairie chicken in Kansas was mapped as shown in Figure 3. Since Bennitt (1939:495) and Schwartz (1945:23) have ascertained that the greater prairie chicken is absent where there are no permanent grasslands, the presence of native grasslands was used to establish the margins of the range of this species in areas where the bird was reported to be present. The mapping all was initially done in the field on county maps with a scale of one-half inch to one mile.

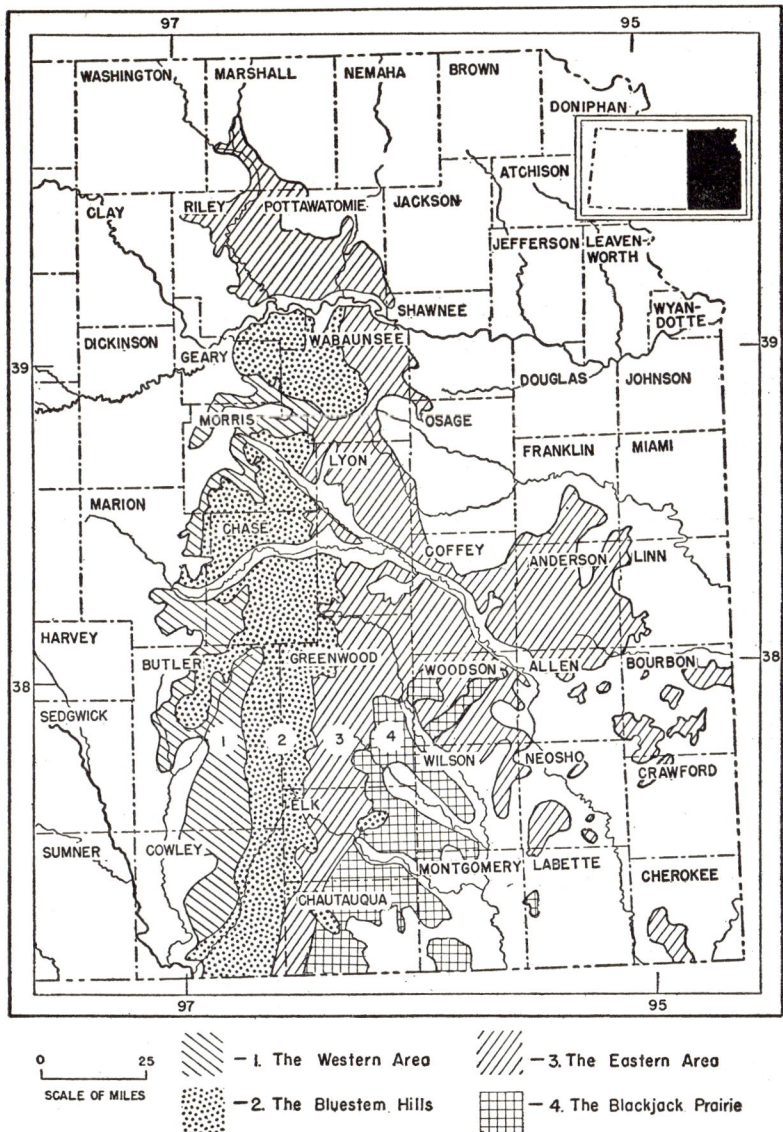

Fig. 3. The principal range of the greater prairie chicken in Kansas. (1) The Western Area; (2) the Bluestem Hills; (3) the Eastern Area; (4) the Blackjack Prairie. Scattered flocks occur in other counties included in the range in Figure 2.

The principal range of the greater prairie chicken is classified into four types, each a modification of Fly's (1946) Natural Agricultural Resource Areas of Kansas (see Figure 3). Data concerning farm crops from townships representative of each type for 1950 were obtained from the files of the Kansas Crop and Livestock Reporting Service, 203 Federal Building, Topeka, Kansas. These data were gathered by township assessors and were from civil townships varying in size from 13,000 to 66,000 acres. Table 1 lists the minimum, average and maximum per cent of the total farmland in native grass and in feed crops for each range type and for six townships in southeastern Kansas which are considered to be marginal range for the greater prairie chicken. The term "feed crops" as used here includes corn, wheat, sorghum and soy-beans. These four crops provide the chief foods used by the greater prairie chicken in autumn and winter.

TABLE 1. THE PER CENT OF THE TOTAL FARMLAND IN NATIVE GRASS AND IN FEED CROPS

	Grassland			Feed Crops		
	Minimum	Average	Maximum	Minimum	Average	Maximum
Eastern Area	57.49	64.26	71.22	14.57	20.74	28.74
Blackjack Prairie	58.17	75.00	93.18	3.71	13.34	22.94
Bluestem Hills	73.78	86.82	92.65	6.72	7.30	15.69
Western Area	45.25	57.15	69.98	14.62	26.70	37.86
Marginal townships	37.69	43.21	49.87	26.37	33.69	49.68

The names of the subdivisions of the principal range of the greater prairie chicken in Kansas, as hereinafter used, were chosen by me as descriptive of the location or chief characteristic of each subdivision. The "backbone" of the bluestem prairie country in Kansas is a narrow strip extending from the Oklahoma border in Chautauqua and Cowley counties to near Marysville in Marshall County. This area is divisible into two parts. The southeastern part, the Blackjack Prairie Area, is characterized by the presence of woods on some hilltops. The remainder of the area has almost no woody cover on the uplands and is designated as the Bluestem Hills Area. To the east and west of these areas the percentage of the total farmland that is in native grass becomes progressively less with increasing distance. Some areas, extending to the eastern and western borders of the principal range of the greater prairie chicken in Kansas, are designated as the Eastern Area and the Western Area respectively. See figure 3 on page 13.

THE EASTERN AREA (Plate 1, Figure *a*).—This type includes parts of Fly's (*op. cit.*) East Central Prairies, the eastern part of his Bluestem Hills and the eastern part of his Cross Timbers and Interspersed Prairies. The Eastern Area is typified by a mixture of croplands and native grasslands; the grasslands are in excess of fifty per cent of the farmland. Croplands are rarely more than one mile from any part of the grasslands; consequently there is a favorable interspersion of winter food and cover. The burning of pastures is practiced but, because roads and croplands act as barriers, fire usually is limited to small areas. This type of range includes the best range for the greater prairie chicken in Kansas.

BLACKJACK PRAIRIE (Plate 1, Figure *b*).—This is the central part of the area designated by Fly (*op. cit.*) as "Cross Timbers and Interspersed Prairies." The soils are sandy, and there are woods on many hilltops. Areas of prairie are extensive and in some places are farther removed from feed crops than in the Eastern Area.

BLUESTEM HILLS (Plate 1, Figure *c*).—This type includes only the central part of Fly's (*op. cit.*) area of the same name. Soils are flinty or cherty, cultivation is limited to the creek valleys, and areas of grassland may be several miles across, resulting, in many places, in poor interspersion of food and cover. Burning of pastures in the spring is common, especially on leased land, and large continuous areas are burned. In the spring of 1950 I drove from Cassoday to Cottonwood Falls, a distance of 24 miles, in this range type without seeing any unburned grassland. The greater prairie chicken was seen twice on this same trip. Spring burning and poor interspersion of winter food and cover are primary limiting factors for the greater prairie chicken in this large area. The Bluestem Hills differ from the Blackjack Prairie in having more extensive grasslands, no woody vegetation on the upland, and in having a calcareous parent material for the soil. Unless further investigation reveals that these two areas differ markedly in the abundance of the greater prairie chicken, they might be considered as a unit when a management plan is put into effect.

WESTERN AREA (Plate 4, Figure *a*).—This type is the transition between the Bluestem Hills and the intensively cultivated land to the west. The agricultural characteristics resemble those of the Eastern Area, except that the grass-flora of the uplands, when grazed, tends strongly toward the short- and the mid-grasses.

Marginal Townships.—Six townships, where the greater prairie chicken occurs in small numbers, were studied to ascertain the per cent of feed crops and of grasslands in areas of marginal quality for this bird. These findings appear in Table 1.

Optimum Townships.—The areas of greatest abundance of the greater prairie chicken in Kansas are in southwestern Anderson County, southwestern Coffey County and northwestern Woodson County. Two townships characteristic of the best of this range were studied to determine the pattern of land use that is optimum for the greater prairie chicken. The summary of land use is as follows:

Anderson County, Welda Township
    Per cent in grass.................................. 62.87
    Per cent in feed crops............................. 18.64
Woodson County, Center Township
    Per cent in grass.................................. 66.35
    Per cent in feed crops............................. 16.64

It is evident that approximately one-third of the land must be in permanent grass to provide the minimum requirements for the greater prairie chicken in Kansas, and that approximately two-thirds in permanent grass provides the optimum condition. The findings relative to the minimum requirements are in close agreement with those of Schwartz (1945:23) for Missouri, but he found no correlation above the minimum between the amount of grassland and the number of prairie chickens. It will be shown later that the Bluestem Hills Area supports fewer prairie chickens than does the Eastern Area. This fact is thought to be the result, at least in part, of the poor interspersion of food and cover in the Bluestem Hills Area in Kansas. See figure 3 on page 13.

Life History of the Greater Prairie Chicken

General Remarks

Earlier workers, notably Bent (1932) and Schwartz (1944 and 1945), have discussed the life history of the greater prairie chicken in detail. In the autumn, flocks or packs assemble and function as a unit in their daily movements throughout the ensuing winter. These packs may be all of one sex or of both sexes. With the advent of warmer weather—anytime from late January to early March—the males separate themselves from the females, and begin to visit places, known as booming-grounds, where territorial disputes and courtship displays take place each morning and evening. The duration and intensity of these disputes and displays depend to some extent on the condition of the weather. In late March the females begin to visit the booming grounds, and usually in the first half of April a peak of mating activity is reached.

Nests are made in dry vegetation left from the previous season. Some sets of eggs hatch before mid-May, but most of them hatch in late May or early June, after an incubation period of 22 or 23 days. Late nests, which are re-nestings after failure of an earlier attempt, hatch as late as July 18, but there are few of these as compared with those that hatch in May and June.

The males continue courtship activities until hot weather, usually until early June. Pursuit of the females is not limited to the booming grounds, but occurs wherever the females are found. As attendance at the booming grounds wanes, the flocks of males disintegrate. The resulting singles and small flocks spend their time loafing about swales and other places where suitable shade is provided by shrubs and tall grass. Females that are not successful in bringing off a brood follow the same routine.

The females that succeed in bringing off a brood stay with their young all summer, and frequent both permanent grasslands and croplands. By the first of September, the young are indistinguishable from the adults, except when the birds are in the hand, and at approximately this time they begin to assemble in flocks.

In the autumn of 1949 a part of Welda Township, Anderson County, was chosen for the intensive study of the life history of the greater prairie chicken. Originally it was planned to use approximately one township for this study, but the density of the population of prairie chickens, and other factors, made it more practical to select a small area where a single flock could be studied in greater detail. The arrangement of roads, fields and farmsteads and the positions of ponds, booming grounds and feeding areas in the Welda Area are shown in figure 4.

Description of the Welda Area

Permanent grasslands used both for pasture and for hay are of native species, predominantly the bluestems, *Andropogon scoparius* Michx. and *A. gerardi* Vitman, the latter occurring mostly in un-

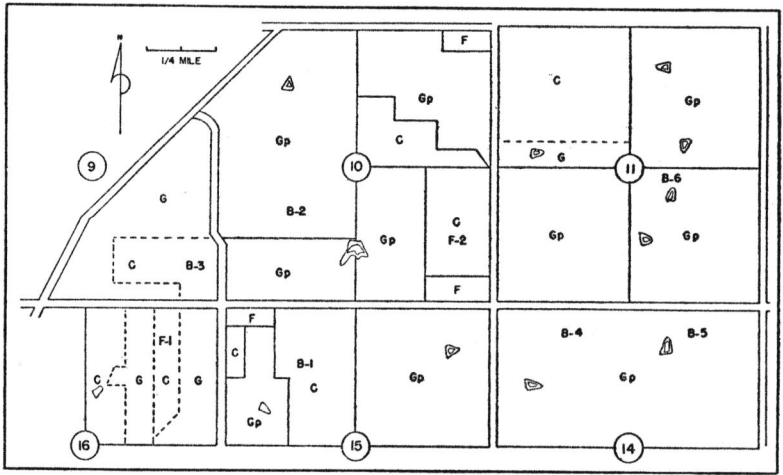

FIG. 4. The Welda Area. Twp. 22S, R. 19E, Anderson County, Kansas. C—cropland; G—grassland used for hay; Gp—grassland used for pasture; F—farmyard; F-1 and F-2—feeding areas; B-1, B-2, etc.—booming grounds. Ponds are represented by irregular enclosed areas and the center of sections by circles.

grazed areas. In most pastures, grazing is well regulated, and good stands of grass occur, but in the northeast quarter of section 15, and about the large pond in section 10, overgrazing by cattle is severe and annual weeds, predominantly ragweeds, *Ambrosia artemisiifolia* L. and *A. bidentata* Michx., blue grass, *Poa pratensis*

L., and annual grasses such as foxtail, *Setaria* sp., form approximately one-half of the ground cover.

In addition to the areas marked as meadow in Figure 4, much of the grass in the well-drained parts of the west half of section 10 was cut for hay each summer. The grassland of sections 9 and 10 was burned each spring in March. No other burning occurred.

The only trees in section 11 and in the north half of section 14, other than an abandoned farm grove and a plum thicket in the northwest quarter of section 11, are six mulberry, *Morus rubra* L., three small white elm, *Ulmus americana* L., and one cottonwood, *Populus deltoides* Marsh. A hedgerow of Osage orange, *Maclura pomifera* Raf., and other hardwoods and cedar, *Juniperus virginiana* L., extends along the west side of the road between sections 10 and 11, and along the north side of the field designated as F-2. There is another hedge of Osage orange along the west side of the pasture in the northwest quarter of section 15. Other woody growth in the western part of the area consists of widely scattered mulberry trees, cottonwoods and elms, and shrubs along the waterways. These shrubs are predominantly false indigo, *Amorpha fruticosa* L., and buttonbush, *Cephalanthus occidentalis* L.

Sources of water were plentiful, because rainfall was normal or above normal each summer, and pools of water occurred at frequent intervals in all waterways.

Cultivated crops in 1949, 1950 and 1951 were sorghums of different varieties, corn, wheat, oats, soybeans and alfalfa. White clover and Korean lespedeza occurred in the pastures. Each cultivated area was subdivided, and crops were rotated within each such area. As a result the same feed crops were available in each area used by the prairie chickens for feeding each year. The northwest quarter of section 15 changed ownership in 1949, and has been more intensively farmed since that year. Terraces were built in the large cultivated area of this quarter in the fall of 1950.

Approximately 22 per cent of the area of study was in cultivation, 77 per cent in grassland and the remainder of the area in farmyards.

Daily Routine of One Flock

The flock (hereinafter referred to as Flock A), resident in the western part of the Welda Area, was observed periodically throughout the period of study, November 8, 1949 to May 1, 1952. Observations were made from a blind and from an automobile at booming grounds and feeding places with the aid of 7×50 binoculars or a 20 power telescope. Records were kept of all observed flock-movements. Color banding of birds trapped and released, and subsequent sight records and returns supplemented these observations. Further information was obtained concerning roosting places and general activity of the birds by walking through the area. Flock A was composed entirely of males and contained 145 birds in the fall of 1949; it declined to 15 birds by the spring of 1952.

In the fall and winter of 1949-1950, the daily routine of Flock A began with a flight from the roosting grounds on unmown slopes in the southwest quarter of section 10. This flight to booming ground number one (B-1) usually occurred approximately one-half hour before sunrise, but was later on days with inclement weather. After a few minutes to an hour there, where some birds would feed in the adjacent cornfield, the flock would fly west to the cultivated land in the northeast quarter of section 16 (F-1), where the principal morning feeding would be done on waste cane and soybeans.

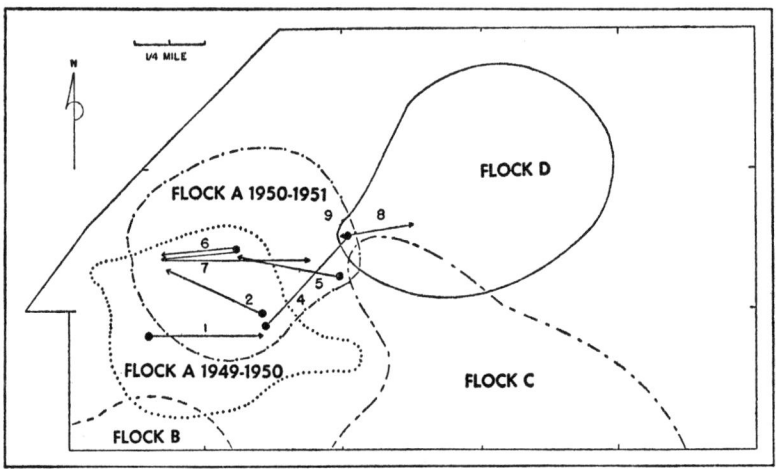

Fig. 5. The usual ranges of four flocks of greater prairie chickens using the Welda Area in winter, and the movements of banded birds (*cf.* Fig. 8). Banding sites are indicated by dots and the movements of banded birds by arrows.

After the flock fed, the birds would return to the vicinity of the roosting area, or to a similar site, where the middle of the day would be spent loafing. In the evening, the feeding area and the booming ground would again be visited, but not in so regular an order as in the morning. The birds returned to the roost usually when it was too dark to observe them well, except against the western sky.

The routine of this flock in 1950-1951 was of the same pattern, but booming ground number two (B-2), and the feeding area in the southeast quarter of section ten (F-2) were used to the exclusion of those formerly used. These changes in daily habits of this flock concurred with the terracing of B-1 and the 1950 hunting season. Each year the range of daily activity of Flock A covered approximately one square mile, but the composite range for the two years was approximately one and one-half square miles. The flocks using the Welda Area are shown in figure 5.

To the southwest, outside the study area, there was another booming ground. Birds from the vicinity of this booming ground (Flock B) fed, in part, at F-1 with Flock A, but the two flocks were distinct at other times. Birds from the vicinity of B-4 and B-5 (Flock C) fed with Flock A at F-2 but the chief range of Flock C was to the south where it fed outside the area. Another flock (Flock D) came from the east to feed at F-2. This flock was thought to be composed of females; as many as 20 females were seen at F-2 at one time. This was the approximate size of Flock D.

Trapping proved to be extremely difficult because of the mild winters and abundant food; the greater prairie chickens seldom came to the bait placed to entice them into traps. Even so, ten birds were trapped and banded. One of these was taken in a tip-top trap (see Hamerstrom, 1942:7), four were taken in a projected net trap (see Dill and Thornsberry, 1950), and five in hoop net traps powered by rat traps of the snap-type. Colored bands and numbered aluminum bands were used in combination so that each banded bird could be identified if observed at close range. Sight records on booming grounds or returns from dead birds, or both, were obtained from eight of these ten birds. The movements of individual birds, made evident by these records, are shown in Figure 5. Bird number one, a male, was trapped at F-1 on December 28, 1949, and was seen at B-1 on March 24, 1950. Birds number two and three were banded at B-1 on October 14 and 19, 1950, respectively. One of these two was seen at B-3 on April 25, 1951. Number four was banded at F-2 on December 16, 1950, and was seen at B-1 on April 24, 1951. Number five was banded at the large pond in the south part of section 10, on December 28, 1950, and was seen repeatedly at B-2 in the spring of 1951. Numbers six and seven were banded at B-2 on March 27 and 30, 1951. Neither returned to B-2, but both were seen at B-3 on April 25, 1951. Number seven was shot approximately 200 yards east of the banding site on October 25, 1951. Numbers eight, nine and ten were banded at F-2 on April 7, 1951. Number nine, the only female banded, was found dead within 200 yards of the banding site on May 3, 1951. Number eight was shot less than one-half mile east of the banding site on October 24, 1951. Number ten was not seen after banding. No banded birds were observed at booming grounds in the spring of 1952.

These observations agree with the observations of flock behavior and together they indicate that different flocks share the same feeding ground, but act as distinct units at other times, and that the daily and seasonal ranges of flocks and individuals were limited to a cruising radius of approximately one-half mile.

These observations stand in contrast to those in Wisconsin of Hamerstrom and Hamerstrom (1949) who found winter packs to be made up of several smaller flocks. These packs operated as units in severe weather but subdivided into smaller groups in mild weather. The ranges of the various packs covered 2-4 square miles and did not overlap. Schwartz (1945:83) found similar behavior in the greater prairie chicken in Missouri. There, flocks of both sexes banded into packs and cruised over most of the range of the separate flocks. In Nebraska, Mohler (1952:22) found the home range of flocks in winter to be 2000 acres (approximately three square miles) or more. These differences in behavior of flocks in winter may be attributed to the mild winter weather that prevailed in the course of this study, and to the greater density of population in the Welda Area.

Activities of Males on the Booming Ground

The activities of the greater prairie chicken on booming grounds have been so completely described by Schwartz (1944 and 1945), and others, that only the observed seasonal changes in activity will be presented here. The earliest autumnal activity on a booming ground was observed three and one-half miles southwest of Ottawa, Franklin County, on September 15, 1949, where 24 males assembled in the morning, engaged in territorial disputes, and unsuccessfully attempted to boom. At the time of the first visit to the Welda Area, on November 8, 1949, approximately 100 males were at B-1 and territorial disputes and booming were in full progress. Attendance at booming grounds was noted at the time of each morning visit by the observer that autumn and winter (1949-1950), and in the next autumn and winter (1950-1951). Schwartz (1945:58) found that the greater prairie chicken in Missouri did not visit booming grounds in mid-winter.

Hamerstrom (1939:108) concluded that activity on booming grounds was determined by upper and lower limits of a combination of light and temperature. This conclusion explains the mid-winter booming-ground activity observed by me in 1949-1950 and

1950-1951, since both winters were mild compared to those when Schwartz made his study. The operation of the upper threshold of light and temperature is indicated by the latest observed booming-ground activity on June 12, 1951, which was a cloudy, cool day. As late as May 30, 1951, spirited booming-ground activities and indications that hens were present on the booming ground were noted.

Summer Activities of Males

In summer, during the molt, males seldom are seen, and they are reluctant to fly when disturbed. Adults of both sexes were observed in low areas where shrubs and associated tall grasses provided favored loafing cover. No evidence was found that the few upland trees were used as loafing cover by adults in summer.

Reproductive Cycle of Females

In winter, too few females were observed to justify drawing definite conclusions as to their activities then. The greater prairie chicken was seen in many places other than the Welda Area, and in all instances males predominated or no females were seen. It seems that the daily routine of females involves fewer conspicuous movements by flight than does that of males.

Although no intensive study of the behavior of females in the breeding season was attempted, such observations as were made merit the same conclusions as those drawn by Schwartz (1945:51). In his discussion of the spring booming-season he concludes, "During the early part of the season the principal activities on the booming ground are territorial disputes and booming. No females are seen there until late in March, when an occasional hen visits the booming ground for a short time. . . . These infrequent visits may continue for a week or more; then suddenly the number of hens visiting on a booming ground increases to a rather constant maximum, marking for several days or a week the so-called height of the season. . . . After this period the number of hens decreases very rapidly to a few who come in only occasionally."

In this study, the earliest observation of a female on a booming ground was on February 25, 1951. The peak of mating, in 1950, occurred in the second week in April. In 1951, although seven mornings were spent observing booming-ground activity from a blind between March 24 and April 25, no peak of mating activity was observed. The largest number of females observed in any one morning, in 1951, was three on April 13.

Hamerstrom (1939:112) concluded that most of the nests of the greater prairie chicken in Wisconsin were begun at the height of the booming-season. Yeatter (1943:385), on the other hand, found that breeding in Illinois was spread more uniformly over a period of time and concluded that this was because all of the birds did not attain sexual readiness at the same time.

Schwartz (1945:53) observed that males remain in their individual territories, on the booming ground, and allow matings in adjacent territories to proceed without interruption only at the height of the breeding season. At other times, males frequently interrupt matings in adjacent territories by driving the male from the back of the female. This is not to imply that all matings occur at the height of the season, for courtship and matings occur at places other than the booming ground, and the spread of hatching dates, including those of re-nestings, indicates that matings occur over at least a six-week period of time. Both sexes seem to become physiologically incapable of breeding shortly after the first of June. This characteristic is most significant, because it limits the reproductive period to late spring and early summer, and makes the success of reproduction largely dependent upon the favorable weather within this short period. Bobwhite quail, on the other hand, remain paired throughout the summer, and have been known to hatch young as late as October. Frequently the main hatch of bobwhites occurs in July. In Missouri, the peak of hatching in quail was in the first half of July in 1948, in the last half of July in 1949, and between July 7 and August 7 in 1950 (see Stanford, 1950 and 1951). The value of the ability thus to persist in nesting is obvious, in that it tends to insure a high reproductive rate even though weather conditions may be unfavorable for nesting and rearing young in the first part of the summer.

Nesting

To find nests and broods of the greater prairie chicken, a flushing device designed after that of Lehmann (1946) was made to be used on a light truck, tractor or jeep. The essential feature of this device was a drag suspended from a horizontal bar that was mounted on the vehicle. The horizontal bar was made of steel pipe in three sections, each ten feet long, the outer two of which telescoped into the center section. A central post provided means of supporting the ends by wires. It was found necessary to use springs in the supporting wires to prevent breakage. The most satisfactory drag was made of pieces of steel pipe the same length as the sections of the horizontal bar. Figure *b* of Plate 4 illustrates this device mounted on a truck. Later, two sections were added making a total spread of 46 feet. This bar on a light tractor was satisfactory. In one instance 160 acres were censused in six hours.

From May 12 to June 19, 1951, 16 nests were found in 610 acres of unburned pastures and meadows. No broods indicative of earlier nests were found, and no nests were found later than June 19 while I was searching for broods with the drag. This tract of 610 acres was given complete coverage and it is thought that all nests were found, because the number of successful nests and the number of broods found agreed closely.

The value of studying nests is sometimes questioned, because of the effects of the disturbance caused by the study. For example, three nests were destroyed by my efforts to find them. My study, otherwise, however, had little effect on the success of nests. No nests were approached on foot, but only in a vehicle. This practice should have minimized any tendency on the part of predators to follow human trails. Hens were difficult to flush from the nest, and in one instance the hen did not flush until the wheel of the truck passed over her tail and pulled out all rectrices and coverts. This hen returned to the nest and succeeded in bringing off her brood. In another instance a hen permitted the wheel of the truck to pass within one foot of one side of the nest and the inner end of the drag to pass within one foot of the other side without flushing. In a third instance, the nest was destroyed by a predator only after the hen had returned and laid two more eggs.

Rate of Egg Laying

Little direct evidence is available as to the rate at which prairie chickens lay eggs. Gross (see Bent, 1932:248) found in nests of captive greater prairie chickens and in one nest of a wild bird that the period of laying was approximately twice as long in days as the number of eggs laid. Lehmann (1941:15) reported that the same species (*T. c. attwateri*) in Texas normally laid one egg per day until the clutch was complete, but that sometimes there were intervals of one to three days between the times of egg-laying. Indirect evidence obtained in this study proves that in some instances egg-laying is at the rate of one egg per day. Two nests found on May 29, 1951, each contained seven unstained eggs plus some stained eggs. The stained eggs had been laid, or were present, in a rainy period. The unstained eggs had been laid after the rains ceased. Examination of the weather data for the Iola weather station, for which hourly readings of precipitation were available, revealed that rain occurred each day from May 16 to 23 inclusive and ended early in the morning of May 23. A light shower recorded at Iola on the 26th did not extend to the study area. If each of these hens had laid one egg per day from May 23 to 29 inclusive, each would have laid seven eggs.

Period of Incubation

Schwartz (1945:66) observed two nests of the greater prairie chicken from the beginning until the end of incubation. The eggs were incubated 23 and 24 days. In my study a nest that was found on May 24, 1951, contained eggs that were incubated at the time of discovery and that hatched 22 or 23 days later.

Success of Nests

Assuming that each hen laid one egg per day, and that the period of incubation is 23 days, the date on which the first egg was laid was calculated for each nest. One or two eggs from each nest were tested in water to determine the stage of incubation (see Westerskov, 1950). For nests that did not hatch, the date on which the first egg was laid was estimated by this means. The fate of each nest is described below. The nests are arranged in the order of the estimated date on which the first egg was laid. All dates refer to 1951.

No. 1. Discovered on May 25, 13 eggs, hit with tractor wheel; salvaged four eggs, one hatched in incubator on May 29.

No. 2. Discovered on May 25, 15 eggs; on June 3 all had hatched at latest by the day before.

No. 3. Discovered on May 25, 13 eggs, hit with tractor wheel; salvaged 8 eggs, hatched in incubator June 1.

No. 4. Discovered on May 25, 13 eggs, hit with tractor wheel; salvaged all eggs, hatched in incubator June 1.

There was one infertile egg among the 39 from nests 1, 3 and 4.

No. 5. Discovered on May 25, 15 eggs; hatched June 6. At 8 A.M. on June 6 the hen was on the nest with the complete brood. The disturbance caused by my marking several of the chicks, the subsequent trampling about by calves, and a heavy rain in the forenoon caused a loss of chicks as follows: one chick trampled in the nest; two stepped on by calves; one dead but no obvious physical damage; one caught by the foot in heavy grass, alive but barely able to move; one sitting quietly near the nest. The two that were alive were taken and successfully reared. The chilled one recovered within 20 minutes after being placed inside my shirt. These two were picked up at 3:15 P.M. when a hen was heard but not seen near the nest.

No. 6. Discovered on May 28, 13 eggs; all hatched on June 3.

No. 7. Discovered on May 26, one egg was cracked; the remaining 13 all hatched on June 9; one live chick left behind in the nest.

No. 8. Discovered on May 24, 12 eggs; all hatched June 16.

No. 9. Discovered on May 24, 8 eggs; all eggs gone without evidence of cause on June 6.

No. 10. Discovered on May 25, 7 eggs; female seen on the nest May 26;

nest had been destroyed on June 3 when the remains of 9 eggs were found. The cause of this loss is uncertain, but tooth marks left on one shell corresponded in width to that between the canine teeth of the raccoon, *Procyon lotor* Linnaeus, or a small dog. According to Stoddard (1931:188), dogs usually eat the entire egg, whereas these eggs had but one side removed in a manner characteristic of the raccoon (see Reardon, 1951).

No. 11. Discovered on May 29, 11 eggs; found destroyed on June 3, canine marks and a tuft of hair on one egg indicated that a spotted skunk, *Spilogale interrupta* Rafinesque, had destroyed the nest (see Plate 4, Figure *c*).

No. 12. Discovered on May 29, 9 eggs; all gone on June 3 without evidence of cause.

No. 13. Discovered on May 28, 2 eggs; found destroyed on June 3, ends of eggs removed and fragments carried off 15 feet from the nest in a manner characteristic of the cotton rat, *Sigmodon hispidus* Say and Ord, as described in Stoddard (1931:140).

No. 14. Discovered on June 16, 9 eggs. On the night of June 29-30 there was a rain of 2.12 inches at Iola (2.33 inches at Garnett). At 11 A. M. on June 30 I visited this nest and found no evidence of the hen; all but two eggs were pipped, at least part of the chicks were alive in the shell. At 4 P. M. the hen was at the nest, and one egg was hatching. On July 2, the shells of two hatched eggs were found here; the other seven had failed to hatch. This nest was situated on the steep side of a natural drainageway. The hen probably was driven from the nest at hatching time by water.

No. 15. Discovered on June 19, 9 eggs; on June 30 all were hatched; the shells were stained and the egg and embryonic membranes were separated from the shells which suggested that they had hatched several days prior to June 30.

No. 16. Discovered on June 14 while I was searching the same area covered on May 25, 9 eggs; never located again; thought to have been destroyed.

Hamerstrom (1939:114) reported that in Wisconsin 50 per cent of the nests were successful. In Illinois, Yeatter (1943:392) found 49 per cent of the nests to be successful. Seven of 16 nests found in this study were successful. Five of these seven were among the first eight when arranged according to the date when the first egg was laid. The remaining three of the first eight are those destroyed by the tractor, all of which were in an advanced stage of incubation, and at least part of which might be presumed to have been successful if undisturbed by me. While it is true that all other unsuccessful nests had incomplete clutches or were in early stages of incubation when found, none of these nests was known to have been abandoned before destruction. The successful nests were found on the first or second, eighth, thirteenth, fourteenth and seventeenth days of incubation, as judged by the dates of hatching.

Size of Clutch

The size of full clutches reported by other observers ranges from a minimum of five (see Hamerstrom, 1939:111) to a maximum of 25 (see Schwartz, 1945:65). The largest clutches were thought by Bent (1932:248) to be the product of two or more hens. The maximum clutch thought to have been produced by one hen is 17 (see Hamerstrom, *loc. cit.*). The average size of 66 clutches in Wisconsin was 12 (Hamerstrom 1939:113).

Audubon (1834:494) noted that second nests had fewer eggs than first nests. Hamerstrom (*loc. cit.*) found that there was a decline in the average size of the clutch as the date on which the first egg was laid was progressively later. A similar decline in size of clutch was noted in the 13 full clutches found in 1951 on the Welda Area. Figure 6 shows the temporal distribution of these clutches, their size and the regression line of size of clutch against date of first egg laid. The regression coefficient, $r = -.702$, represents a high degree of negative correlation between the date of first egg laid and the size of the clutch.

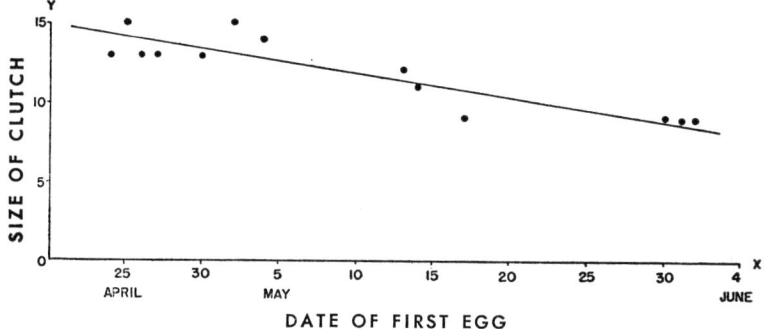

FIG. 6. Scatter diagram of size of clutch (Y axis) plotted against estimated date on which first egg was laid (X axis) and the regression line of Y on X. $r = -.702$. Data from the Welda Area, 1951.

The dates on which first eggs were laid occur in three groups (see Figure 6). The mean intervals between these groups are 16 and 17 days. This grouping suggests that re-nesting occurred after failure of first nests. Hamerstrom (1939:115) found that the greater prairie chicken has certain breeding characteristics in common with the bobwhite quail, which is known to re-nest, and concluded from this that the prairie chicken re-nests. Lehmann (1941:15) found that some Attwater prairie chickens re-nest as many as two times, after failures, for a total of three nesting efforts.

In summary, although the sample is small, it seems clear that early clutches are larger, are more successful, and produce most of the young. Sixty-eight of the 79 chicks that were produced from 16 nests came from the earliest eight nests. As Lehmann (1941:15) says relative to the Attwater prairie chicken, "A successful season depends largely on the fate of the early nests, so that a primary objective of management should be to safeguard these attempts."

Decline in Size of Broods

In 1950, when I was unable to be on the study area, Mr. William Brecheisen, Jr. recorded all broods seen in the course of his normal farming operations. He did not estimate ages of the chicks after they were half grown, and the data that he gathered can best be treated according to the date of observation. The results of his observations, presented in Figure 7, reveal that broods ranged in size from three to fifteen, averaged approximately eight chicks at the beginning of the season and averaged 6.6 at the end of the season in August.

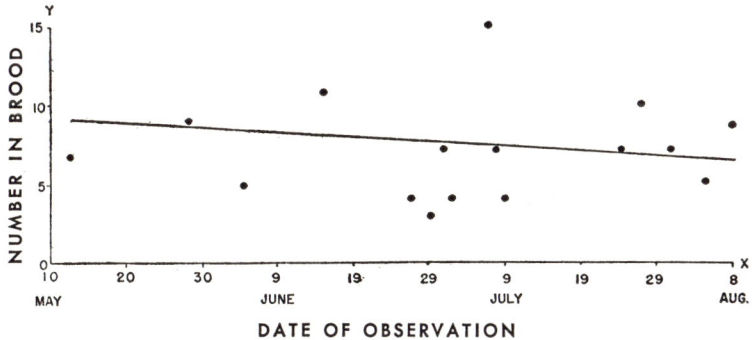

FIG. 7. Scatter diagram of size of brood seen (Y axis) plotted against the date of observation (X axis) and the regression line of Y on X. $r = -.191$. Data from the Welda Area, 1950.

In 1951, the flushing device previously described was used to find broods in pastures; and early morning work with a dog located broods in cultivated land where the flushing device could not be used. Six hundred and twenty acres of the study area, plus eighty acres outside the area, were censused. A total of eighteen broods able to fly were found ranging in number of individuals per brood from two to twelve. Figure 8 presents the distribution and decline in size of these broods. The average number of individuals per brood was four and one-half as compared with approximately seven in 1950. The decline in number of individuals per brood, after the young were able to fly, was less than in 1950, $r = -.091$ in 1951 as compared to $r = -.191$ in 1950. Another difference between the two seasons was that the first broods were seen 19 days earlier in 1950.

If it is true that breeding activity is controlled by a combination of light and temperature (see Hamerstrom, 1939:108), then a comparison of the average temperature and cloudiness, as reflected by the total precipitation, in the two winters might help to explain the 19-day delay in hatching in 1951. Presumably, the three months before the normal onset of breeding activity would affect this phenomenon. In 1950, the temperature was 1.3 degrees above normal for this period and the precipitation was 2.02 inches below normal (normal is 4.37). In 1951, the temperature was 2.7 degrees below normal and the precipitation was 0.82 inches above normal for the same period. Thus, the combination of light and temperature was presumably less in 1951. While a study over a much longer period of time, employing more refined techniques for measuring the amount of light, would be necessary to justify drawing any definite conclusions, these data do indicate that the winter weather in 1951 might have delayed the onset of breeding.

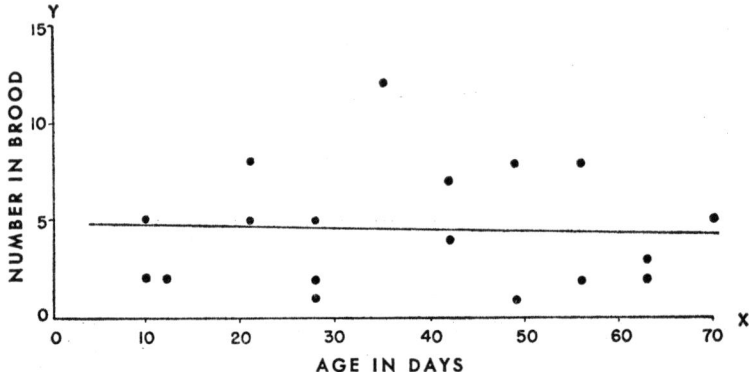

Fig. 8. Scatter diagram of size of brood seen (Y axis) plotted against estimated age of brood in days (X axis) and regression line of Y on X. r = —.091. Data are from the Welda Area, 1951.

The smaller size of the broods observed in 1951 probably was a result of the unusually heavy precipitation. Schwartz (1945:67) called attention to the destructive effects of heavy rain in the hatching period. In 1951, the average size of clutches in successful nests was 12 eggs; nevertheless at the time when the chicks were able to fly, approximately ten days of age, the average brood contained less than five chicks (approximately eight in 1950). Precipitation in June of 1951 was 12.04 inches at Garnett. This is 7.30 inches above normal for this part of eastern Kansas. Precipitation and temperature in the same period of 1950 were near normal.

In summary, in most years, and possibly in every year, the most critical time for the greater prairie chicken in Kansas seems to be when nesting and rearing of the young occur, namely from the middle of May until the middle of July.

PLUMAGES OF THE GREATER PRAIRIE CHICKEN
Development of Plumage in the Young

Little is known of the details of the molt in prairie chickens, because only in rare instances have prairie chickens been successfully reared in captivity whereby birds of known age were available for study. Lehmann (1941:16) gives an account of the growth of the Attwater prairie chicken based on observations of wild birds.

Dwight (1900:164) observed that the postjuvenal molt in prairie chickens is complete except for the two outermost primaries. The condition of these two primaries was used by Ammann (1944) in differentiating between birds of the year and adults in autumn populations. Petrides and Nestler (1943 and 1952) developed techniques for aging young bobwhites by noting the condition of the molt of the remiges. This technique is a valuable tool in determining the time of the major hatch in wild birds—an important determination in the study of population dynamics.

Twenty-five eggs of the greater prairie chicken, salvaged from nests 1, 3 and 4, were placed in an incubator at 103° F. Seventeen chicks hatched from these eggs and were placed in an electrically heated brooder. The newly hatched chicks fed readily on insects, including mealworms, and some learned to eat commercial chick feed. Others did not learn to eat, and seven died by the fourth day after hatching. Moistened chick mash and lettuce leaves were the staple foods of those that survived after the fourth day.

The legs and joints of some birds that survived after the fourth day became swollen (Plate 2, Figure *d*). In some individuals the use of one leg was lost. After the fourth day, birds were sacrificed at intervals to the 29th day. In the meantime, two chicks taken from nest number 5 were placed in the brooder, and later were reared. One died at the age of 18 weeks and the other one was released at the point of capture at the age of 20 weeks.

Insofar as possible these captive birds were examined once each week, but after the twelfth week it was not possible to handle them without undue risk of injury to them. In each examination, the length of each remex was taken by placing the end of a rule against the insertion of the feather in the skin and flattening the feather against the rule. Supplementary information was obtained from seven wild-taken juvenal greater prairie chickens. The condition of the molt was noted for each and the remiges were measured according to the same system as was used for the captive birds.

Pterylosis of the greater prairie chicken is essentially the same as that of the ruffed grouse as described by Trainer and Holm (see Bump et al., 1947:76-90 and 741). Terminology used herein is the same as that used by Trainer and Holm except that the primaries are numbered from proximal to distal, the terms supra-ocular and infra-ocular are used to denote the areas immediately above and below the eye and that the term "cervical apteria" is used to designate the bare areas on the sides of the neck.

Because the number of birds available for study was small it is impossible to infer the probable amount of variation that occurs between individuals, and thus to determine the extent to which the data may be used in estimating the ages of birds in the field. However, the results do form a tentative scale for aging immature greater prairie chickens. In the following descriptions, emphasis is placed on the changes that occur as the birds become older. All measurements of primary feathers and secondary feathers are given in numerical order. The number of each specimen is the catalogue number of the University of Kansas Museum of Natural History. The unnumbered specimens are the two captives.

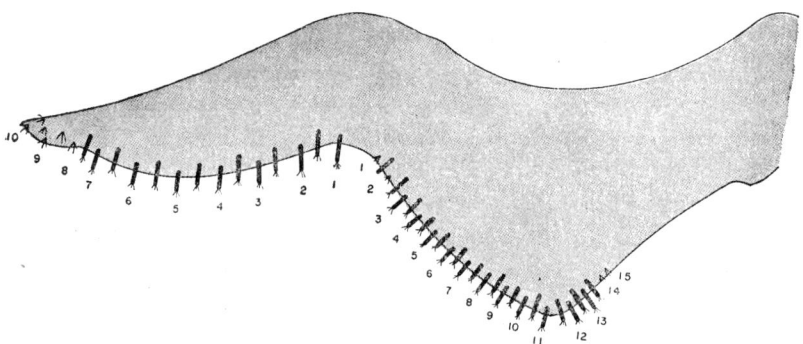

FIG. 9. Condition of the remiges of the greater prairie chicken at hatching. Sheaths of juvenal primary feathers 1-7 and their greater upper coverts are present. Sheaths of juvenal secondary feathers 3-13 and juvenal greater upper coverts 1-13 are present. All other remiges are present as natal down, and down feathers remain attached to the tips of the sheaths.

Twelve hours. No. 30473 KU (Figure 9). Natal down throughout, except on the alar tract where there are, of the juvenal plumage, primaries 1-7, greater primary coverts 2-7, secondaries 3-13 and greater secondary coverts 1-13; all juvenal feathers are sheathed and are of approximately same length, 7 mm.

Thirty-six hours. No. 30474 KU. Sheaths of primaries extend beyond the down.

Sixty hours. No. 30475 KU. Primaries 2-7 unsheathed at tips; greater primary coverts unsheathed at tips; secondaries and their coverts still sheathed; juvenal feathers of alula present and sheathed.

Sixty-six hours. No. 30492 KU. No appreciable change from condition at sixty hours.

Eighty hours. No. 30476 KU. Lengths of first seven primaries 6, 9, 10, 9, 8, 6, 4 mm.; juvenal scapulars present and sheathed.

Eighty-five hours. No. 30477 KU. Primary one unsheathed at tip; lengths of primaries 9, 10, 10, 11, 12, 11, 7 mm.; greater coverts cover base of primaries; lesser primary coverts present and beginning to unsheath; juvenal feathers of alula unsheathed (visible in Plate 2, Figure *b*).

Four days. No. 30479 KU. Lengths of primaries 9, 10, 10, 11, 11, 12, 10 mm.; secondaries unsheathed at tips.

Six days. No. 30478 KU. Lengths of primaries 20, 22, 28, 28, 28, 26, 22 mm.; juvenal scapulars unsheathed at tips.

Eight days. No. 30482 KU. Lengths of primaries 25, 30, 30, 32, 30, 27, 23 mm.; first juvenal feathers of sternal region present, sheathed; neither juvenal scapulars nor sternal feathers yet visible through undisturbed down.

Ten days. No. 34083 KU. Lengths of primaries 33, 36, 37, 38, 39, 33, 29, 11 mm.; primary eight present for first time; juvenal scapulars unsheathed at tips; most advanced juvenal feathers of sternal region unsheathed at tips; superior margins of sternal region and of femoral tract with quills of juvenal feathers (visible in Plate 2, Figure *c*).

Eleven days. No. 30484 KU. Lengths of primaries 38, 39, 40, 38, 40, 38, 33, 9 mm.; juvenal feathers of dorsal cervical region and of interscapular region now present and sheathed; appearance of new juvenal feathers in sternal region progressing ventrad.

Thirteen days. No. 30485 KU. Lengths of primaries 50, 51, 52, 52, 49, 48, 40, 20 mm.; no appreciable change otherwise.

Fifteen days. No. 30486 KU. Growth complete in juvenal primaries 1-3, lengths as at 13 days, lengths of others 57, 54, 50, 46, 20 mm.; a few sheaths of juvenal feathers on coronal region; in cervical region, sheaths of juvenal feathers present from base of neck to posterior border of cervical apteria; juvenal feathers of interscapular region unsheathed and concealing down; sheaths of juvenal feathers of posterior dorsal region present, but hidden in down; juvenal rectrices present and unsheathed, juvenal feathers of sternal region in paired patches, the sheathed feathers meeting at midline (see Plate 2, Figures *c* and *d*).

Twenty-two days. No. 30487 KU. Lengths of primaries 48, 62, 60, 66, 71, 71, 65, 42 mm.; primaries 9-10 visible in flesh; a few unsheathed juvenal feathers on midline of coronal region; juvenal auriculars present; juvenal dorsal cervicals extend to above cervical apteria; juvenal feathers of posterior dorsal region cover down; juvenal rectrices average 28 mm. long; juvenal undertail-coverts equal rectrices; juvenal ventral cervicals extend to below cervical apteria; sternal region covered with juvenal feathers except at midline (see Plate 2, Figure *c*).

Twenty-nine days. No. 30488 KU. Juvenal primary 1 replaced; primary one sheathed, 14 mm. long; lengths of primaries 2-10 are 60, 72, 82, 86, 90, 82, 68, 25, 13 mm.; coronal and occipital regions with juvenal feathers of

[33]

characteristic russet color; auriculars pronounced; juvenal cervicals present to anterior border of cervical apteria; juvenal restrices average 45 mm. long; juvenal plumage complete on sternal region and femoral tract; crural and pedal tracts with sheathed juvenal feathers throughout (see Plate 2, Figure f).

The following descriptions are based on notes made from captive birds and deal primarily with postjuvenal molt of wing.

Forty-one days. Male. Lengths of first-winter primaries 1-2, 77 and 32 mm.; first-winter primary number 3 visible in flesh; juvenal primaries 4-8 completely grown; primaries 9-10, 64 and 36 mm. long; juvenal pinnae slightly longer than other cervicals. Female. Primaries in same stage of replacement as in male; first-winter primaries 1-2, 71 and 45 mm. long; juvenal primaries 9-10, 52 and 39 mm. long; both specimens with plumage of head slightly advanced over that of 29-day-old birds, but natal down still evident; no postjuvenal molt on body (see Plate 3, Figure b).

Forty-eight days. Male. First-winter primaries 1-4, 87, 73, 62, 20 mm. long; juvenal primaries 5-10, 89, 96, 109, 115, 86, 62 mm. long; first-winter secondary number 3, 29 mm. long; other secondaries juvenal. Female. Molt of primaries same as in male. Lengths of primaries 82, 93, 57, 17, 113, 115, 124, 128, 86, 65 mm.; molt of secondaries same as in male; secondary number 3, 32 mm. long (see Plate 3, Figure c).

Fifty-five days. Female. First-winter primaries 1-5, 97, 97, 78, 60, 15 mm. long and all growing; juvenal primaries 6-10, 92, 108, 122, 102, 70 mm. long; 9-10 growing; first-winter secondaries 3-4, 52 and 37 mm. long; all other secondaries juvenal and grown (see Plate 3, Figure d).

Sixty days. Male. First-winter primaries 1-5, 96, 108, 108, 88, 52 mm. long; number 6 missing; juvenal primaries 7-10, 115, 132, 113, 87 mm. long; first-winter secondaries 3-5, 86, 64, 20 mm. long; greater secondary coverts 1-8 of first-winter plumage. Female. Molt of primaries same as in male. Primaries 93, 97, 92, 77, 45, 0, 100, 120, 100, 83 mm. long; primary coverts 1-5 replaced; first-winter secondaries 3-5, 75, 55, 15 mm. long; greater secondary coverts 1-7 of first-winter plumage.

Sixty-seven days. Female. First-winter primaries 1-6, 98, 102, 110, 112, 87, 44 mm. long; juvenal primaries 7-10, 100, 121, 128, 98 mm. long; 9-10 growing; first-winter secondaries 3-6, 82, 48, 38, 10 mm. long and growing.

Seventy-five days. Male. First-winter primaries 1-7, 96, 102, 120, 136, 110, 96, 20 mm. long; juvenal primaries 8-10, 110, 146, 116 mm. long; 9 and 10 growing.

Eighty-two days. Male. First-winter primaries 1-8, 105, 124, 128, 140, 165, 160, 110, 30 mm. long; juvenal primaries 9-10, 152 and 125 mm. long; secondary 1 juvenal; 2-10 first-winter and nearly grown. Female. First-winter primaries 1-7, 100, 105, 111, 121, 143, 128, 67 mm. long; 8 missing; juvenal primaries 9-10, 137 and 115 mm. long and fully grown; secondary 1 juvenal; number 2 first-winter and 38 mm. long; 3-4 first-winter and grown; 5-8 first-winter and 86, 78, 56, 26 mm. long and growing; other secondaries juvenal (see Plate 3, Figure e).

One hundred and twenty-six days. No. 30472 KU. Male. Primaries 105, 114, 125, 142, 170, 178, 176, 166, 152, 124 mm. long; 1-8 first-winter, 9-10 juvenal; only number 8 growing; secondaries all replaced and 88, 102, 101, 101, 99, 99, 96, 96, 94, 94, 92, 91, 88 mm. long; all other tracts in complete first-winter plumage but with growing feathers throughout.

PLATE 1

Fig. *a*. Mixed farmland and native grassland typical of the Eastern Area. Near Mildred, Allen County, Kansas, April 14, 1952. Photo No. 44 KUMNH.

Fig. *b*. Oak thicket in extensive grassland in the Blackjack Prairie. Eight miles N Fall Riv., Greenwood Co., Kan., July 14, 1952. Photo No. 45 KUMNH.

Fig. *c*. Extensive pasture land typical of the Bluestem Hills. One mile west of Eskridge, Wabaunsee County, Kansas, July 13, 1952. Photo No. 46 KUMNH.

PLATE 2

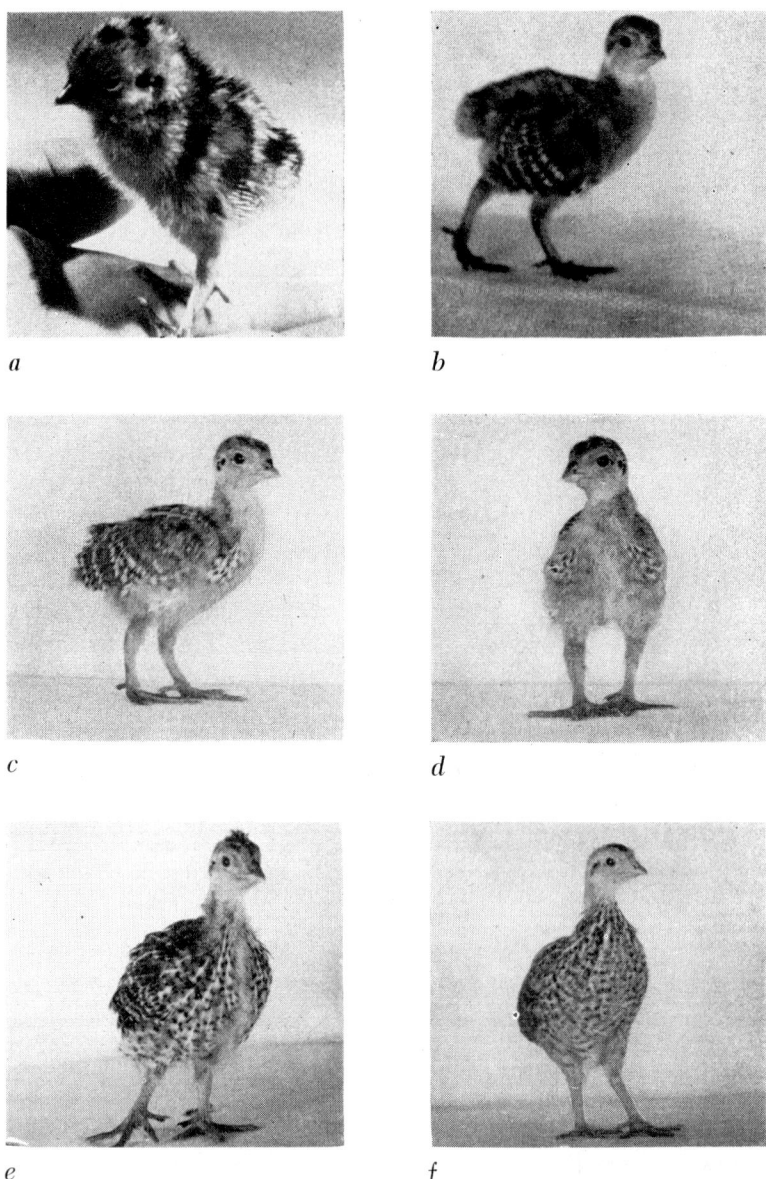

Juveniles of the greater prairie chicken one day to four weeks of age. (*a*) one-day-old, plumage completely of natal down; (*b*) one-week old, remiges and alula unsheathed; (*c* and *d*) two-weeks old, note conspicuous juvenal feathers of the breast; (*e*) three-weeks old, sternal feathers do not meet at the middle; (*f*) four-weeks old, breast is fully feathered. Photo *a* by Robert Rose, Photos *b* to *f* are Nos. 52 to 56 KUMNH respectively.

PLATE 3

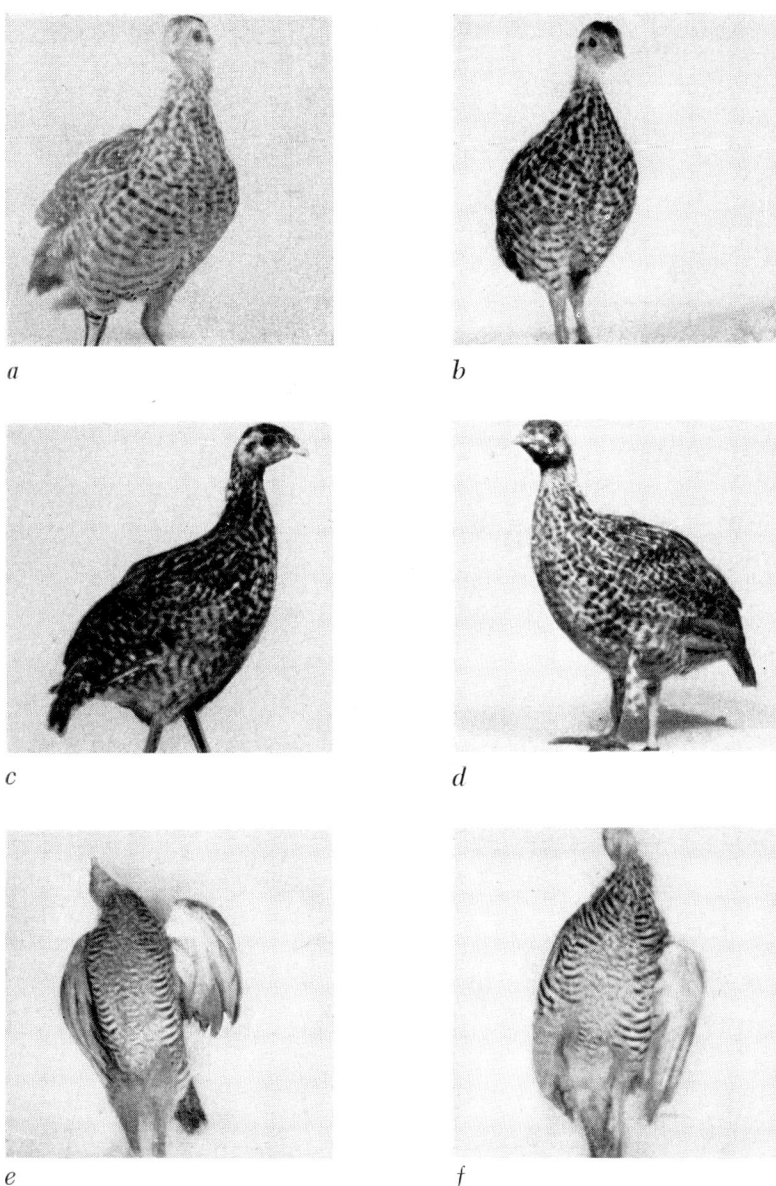

Juveniles of the greater prairie chicken. (a) five-weeks old, juvenal plumage appears complete except for head and legs; (b) six-weeks old, juvenal feathers are appearing on upper neck and head; (c) seven-weeks old, juvenal plumage nearly complete; (d) eight-weeks old, juvenal plumage is complete; (e) a captive bird eleven-weeks old; (f) a specimen from the Welda Area with stage of molt of the wing the same as e, note the similarity of the molt of the breast in e and f. Photos Nos. 58, 60, 62, 63, 64, and 66 KUMNH.

PLATE 4

Fig. *a*. Mixed farmland and grassland typical of the Western Area. Seven mi. W Bazaar, Chase County, Kansas, July 13, 1952. Photo No. 47 KUMNH.

Fig. *b*. Flushing-bar mounted on a State Biological Survey truck. Welda Area, June 13, 1951. Photo No. 48 KUMNH.

Fig. *c*. Nest No. 11 after destruction by a spotted skunk. Welda Area, June 3, 1952. Photo No. 51 KUMNH.

The sequence of molt of the body plumage can be described more accurately from freshly killed specimens than from live birds, or from dried skins. The condition of the molt was noted in seven freshly killed young greater prairie chickens in the summer of 1951. The notes made from these birds form the basis for the following descriptions.

No. 30490 KU. Male. Molt of primaries slightly advanced over that of birds forty-one days old. First-winter primaries 1-3, 95, 66, 21 mm. long; juvenal primaries 4-10, 89, 96, 99, 110, 106, 54, 40 mm. long; primaries 1, 2, 3, 8, 9, 10 growing; secondaries all juvenal; interramal, infra-ocular and supra-ocular regions with natal down; pedal tract with sheathed juvenal feathers; all other regions juvenal.

No. 30469 KU. Female. Primary replacement same as in female fifty-five days old. First-winter primaries 1-5, 106, 112, 97, 62, 11 mm. long; juvenal primaries 6-10, 111, 122, 133, 112, 87 mm. long; first-winter secondaries 3-4, 31 and 5 mm. long; other secondaries juvenal; capital tract juvenal throughout; cervical and interscapular regions with first-winter feathers interspersed with juvenal feathers; no replacement in posterior dorsal region; three central rectrices missing (thought to be accidental); ventral tract with first-winter feathers throughout, not showing beyond juvenal feathers except at superior margin of sternal region; femoral and crural tracts with first-winter feathers as sheaths, not visible beyond juvenal feathers.

No. 30470 KU. Male. A sick bird from same brood as No. 30469 KU. First-winter primaries 1-5, 105, 105, 109, 93, 36 mm. long; juvenal primaries 6-10, 115, 125, 128, 109, 80 mm. long; first-winter secondaries 3-4, 79 and 36 mm. long; otherwise as in No. 30469 KU except all rectrices present.

No. 30493 KU. Male. Primary replacement same as in two birds sixty days old. First-winter primaries 1-5, 107, 115, 112, 84, 41 mm. long; primary 6 missing; juvenal primaries 7-10, 126, 140, 125, 89 mm. long; primaries 3, 4, 5, 9, and 10 growing; first-winter secondaries 3-5, 83, 34, 10 mm. long; capital tract juvenal; first-winter sheaths present on cervical region and scapular tract; posterior dorsal region with first-winter feathers except posteriorly; no replacement in caudal tract; first-winter feathers visible on ventral tract from between cervical apteria to anterodorsal sternal region and to femoral tract; some first-winter sheaths hidden in juvenal feathers on midline anteriorly but not posteriorly.

No. 30495 KU. Male. Primary replacement same as in male seventy-five days old. First-winter primaries 1-7, 112, 118, 118, 130, 111, 66, 10 mm. long; juvenal primaries 8-10, 127, 136, 114 mm. long; primaries 5, 6, 7, 9 and 10 growing; secondary 1 juvenal and 83 mm. long; secondary 2 missing; first-winter secondaries 3-9, 113, 116, 83, 65, 53, 36, 21 mm. long; secondaries 5-9 growing; greater primary coverts 1-7 replaced; greater secondary coverts all replaced, grading in condition of growth from fully grown distally to unsheathed at tip only proximally; under primary and secondary coverts present as sheaths; capital tract and anterior cervical region all juvenal, otherwise spinal tract with first-winter feathers throughout; two central rectrices missing (thought to be accidental); first-winter sternals meet at midline anteriorly but not posteriorly; abdominals, crurals and pedals juvenal.

No. 30489 KU. Male. Primary replacement same as in female eighty-two days old. First-winter primaries 1-7, 114, 116, 120, 140, 164, 150, 90 mm. long; primary 8 missing; juvenal primaries 9-10, 161 and 156 mm. long; primaries 6-7 growing; secondary 1 missing; first-winter secondaries 2-13, 117, 110,

110, 110, 108, 106, 102, 89, 77, 65, 45, 24 mm. long; capital tract with first-winter feathers on coronal region, juvenal feathers elsewhere; dorsal and ventral cervical feathers of first-winter plumage to anterior border of cervical apteria, remainder of spinal tract completely of first winter feathers except juvenal feathers interspersed in interscapular region; rectrices juvenal; upper tail-coverts of first-winter feathers; undertail-coverts of juvenal feathers; ventral tract with first-winter feathers meeting at midline anteriorly, extending posteriorly along superior margin to femoral tract; abdominal region with a few first-winter feathers posteriorly, otherwise with juvenal feathers (see Plate 3, Figure *f*); femoral and crural tracts predominantly of first-winter feathers; pedals juvenal.

Summary of Molt.—The postnatal and postjuvenal molts occur in the same sequence. Juvenal primaries 1-7 are present at hatching and subsequently 8, 9 and 10 appear in that order. Juvenal primary number 1 is molted at four weeks of age, and at that age juvenal primaries 9 and 10 appear. Molt of the primaries proceeds distally, and on the average one feather is molted in each wing each week. Number 8 is molted at twelve weeks of age. Numbers 9 and 10 are retained through the first winter. The greater primary coverts are replaced in the same sequence and approximately at the same time as the corresponding primaries.

Secondaries 3-13 are present at hatching, and all are present in the juvenal plumage at the age of six weeks. The postjuvenal molt of the secondaries begins with number 3 and proceeds proximally, but with more variation between individuals than there is in the order of appearance of the primaries. Secondaries 2 and 1 are lost in that order when the postjuvenal molt of the primaries is nearing completion at approximately ten weeks of age.

At the time of hatching, the entire body, head and legs, excepting the apteria, are covered with natal down. As a rule, in a molt, the first feathers to appear in a given region are in the anterior or dorsal part of that region, and growth proceeds posteriad and ventrad. An exception to this is the cervical plumage which appears first on the posterior part of the neck. Posterior dorsal feathers and abdominal feathers appear over the entire region at one time. The first feathers to appear on the body in a molt are the scapulars; they are followed by the sternals, interscapulars and the femorals. The capital, caudal and pedal tracts are the last to molt. The rectrices seemingly are molted all at one time, or nearly so, since no progressive loss of tail feathers is evident in any specimens at hand.

Age Based on the Condition of the Molt

Molt in the young of the greater prairie chicken is an orderly process. On four occasions, greater prairie chickens, too young

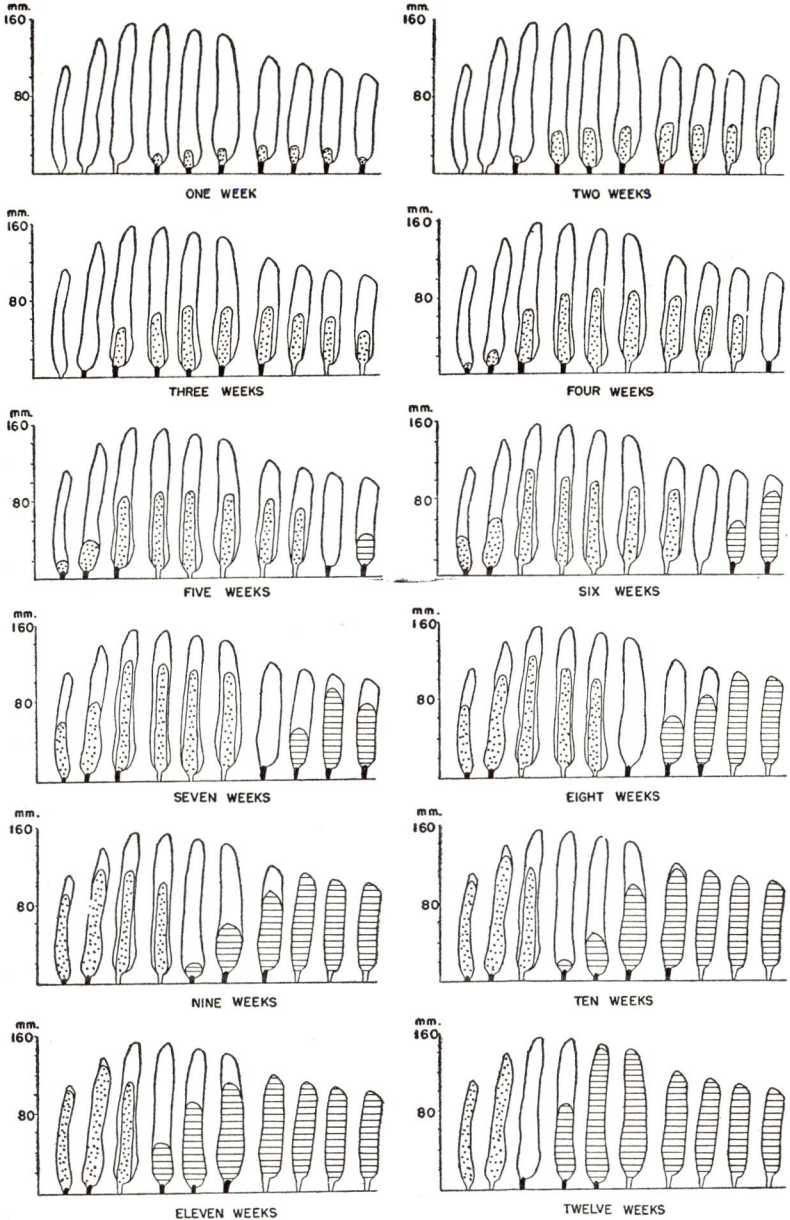

Fig. 10. Condition of the molt of the primaries of the greater prairie chicken one week to twelve weeks of age. Blackened bases of the feathers indicate that the feather is growing; juvenal feathers are stippled and first-winter feathers are cross-barred. Feather number one is at the right in each series of ten primaries.

to fly far, were captured and examined in the field. Comparison of these individuals and the specimens collected in the wild with the captive birds, demonstrates that captives correspond closely with wild birds both in growth and in development of their plumage. Comparison of the wild birds with the captive birds permits the investigator to age the wild birds accurately enough to determine the time of the peak of hatching.

As an aid to ascertaining the age of young prairie chickens, charts illustrating the development of the primaries are presented in Figure 10. Only data from captive birds of known age were used in preparing these charts. For each primary an outline of the fully formed adult feather is shown. Within this outline, the condition of each feather is shown at the age under consideration. A feather which is growing, is indicated by the base of the quill being blackened. Juvenal feathers are shown as stippled, and first-winter feathers are shown as cross barred. The photographs (Pls. 2 and 3) illustrate the condition of the molt of the body at various ages. These photographs are of captive birds, except Plate 3, figure f. These figures demonstrate the close correspondence in body plumage of wild and captive birds with identical condition of molt of the wing.

Molt of the Adult Greater Prairie Chicken

Adult males begin to molt after the cessation of breeding activity. At this time they become secretive and reluctant to fly. No females with broods were collected, but those without broods that were examined corresponded to the males in the progress of molt.

No. 30494 KU. Male. Taken August 25, 1951. Molt of wing and body feathers complete; rectrices not molted; capital and pedal tracts not molted; pinnae replaced and 35 mm. long.

No. 29914 KU. Male. Taken September 15, 1950. All primaries molted, 9-10 present as sheaths; all secondaries molted, number 1, 26 mm. shorter than number 2; rectrices not molted; sheaths of new feathers on throat.

No. 30491 KU. Female. Taken July 25, 1951. Primaries 1-6 replaced, number 6 a sheath; corresponding greater coverts replaced; secondaries 3-4 replaced; number 4 a sheath; new feathers on coronal region; interscapular region with approximately 30 per cent new feathers; posterior dorsal region not replaced; ventral tract with new feathers ahead of wing, otherwise not replaced; caudal tract not replaced.

No. 20 M. F. B. Female. Taken on July 28, 1951. Primaries 1-5 replaced; secondaries not replaced; capital tract and anterior cervical region with only sheaths of new feathers; caudal tract as follows: two outer left, four outer right and central left rectrices old; all others new and of greater length medially. This is the only specimen examined with partial molt of the rectrices.

Summary.—The general pattern of the postnuptial molt seems to be the same as that of the postjuvenal molt, especially of the remiges. The body molt starts near the base of the wings, but may occur rapidly and may be general over the body, with the capital, caudal and pedal tracts being last as in the young.

Length of Primaries as Correlated with Age and Sex

Measurements were taken of primary number eight of each bird, killed by hunters, examined in the open season, on October 24, 1951. This was to ascertain the amount of variation in the length of this feather and to determine whether or not its length might be used as a criterion of sex. Since the age class (adult or immature) can be ascertained by the condition of the two outer primaries, both sex and age could be ascertained from the wing alone if it were possible to separate the sexes by this means. Measurements were taken in millimeters by placing the end of a rule against the hind edge of the wing at the base of the feather and flattening the feather against the rule. Data were obtained from 206 birds, and were recorded with the classification of each bird as to sex and age. To aid in the interpretation of these data, wings were saved from 23 birds, and measurements were made of both the seventh and eighth primaries of these wings.

TABLE 2. LENGTH CHARACTERISTICS OF PRIMARY FEATHERS OF THE GREATER PRAIRIE CHICKEN (CF. FIG. 11). $\overline{X} \pm 2 \frac{s_x}{n}$ IS THE 0.9546 CONFIDENCE LIMITS OF THE MEAN; s_x IS THE STANDARD DEVIATION; V IS THE COEFFICIENT OF VARIATION; n IS THE NUMBER OF INDIVIDUALS IN THE SAMPLE. EXTREMES OF LENGTH ARE IN MILLIMETERS.

	Extremes of Length	$\overline{X} \pm 2 \frac{s_x}{n}$	s_x	V	n
Primary 8	141-172	159.30 ± 3.74	8.99	5.64	23
Primary 7	153-171	162.00 ± 2.54	5.45	3.77	23
All males	138-178	166.29 ± 1.40	7.08	4.26	102
Selected males	151-178	168.89 ± 1.14	5.72	3.43	99
All females	98-178	158.41 ± 1.26	6.42	4.05	104
Selected females	148-178	159.18 ± 1.10	5.51	3.41	100
All adults	142-178	163.78 ± 1.34	7.11	4.34	112
All young	98-178	162.55 ± 1.68	8.13	5.00	94

Variation in the length of the eighth primary was found to occur, and this primary had not completed its growth in some of the birds examined. To compare the variation due to incomplete growth with the variation due to individual differences, primaries seven and eight, from the 23 wings, were compared.

Table 2 and Figure 11 summarize the analyzed data from all the wings that were examined, both in the field and in the laboratory. In the table the data headed "primary 7" and "primary 8" are from the 23 wings examined in the laboratory, and the other data are presented by classes of age and sex. The presentation in Figure 11 is by "Dice squares" which include the range, mean, one standard deviation either side of the mean and two standard errors either side of the mean. Two standard errors either side of the mean represent the 0.9546 confidence limits that may be placed on a given sample. Thus, where these do not overlap, the difference between the means is significant at that level. The coefficient of variation is a measure of the variability—the smaller the coefficient the less the variability.

In the 23 wings, the seventh primary is less variable than is the eighth, $V = 3.77$ as compared to 5.64. This difference is caused by the shortness of the eighth primary in some birds; this shortness is indicated by the longer range below the mean in Figure 19. The pulpy bases of the shafts indicate that these feathers are not completely grown. Contrasted with the data from primary number eight, those for number seven are completely symmetrical (see Figure 11) indicating a normal distribution of primary lengths.

In samples from the field, the lengths of some feathers stood apart from those of others on the lower end of the scale, indicating incomplete growth in those feathers. It seemed reasonable that the data might be refined by dropping these measurements from consideration when comparing lengths of primaries of males and females. This was done, and these categories are indicated as selected males and selected females. It is apparent (see Figure 11) that the average length of primary eight is different between males and females, and that this difference is statistically significant at a high level of confidence, but that the range in length is too great to permit the separation of sexes by this means, even when the lower extremes (incompletely grown feathers) are eliminated as in the instance of the selected groups. The average length of primary number eight is not significantly different between birds-of-the-year and adults in the samples available to me and it is thought that a larger sample would reveal no significant difference.

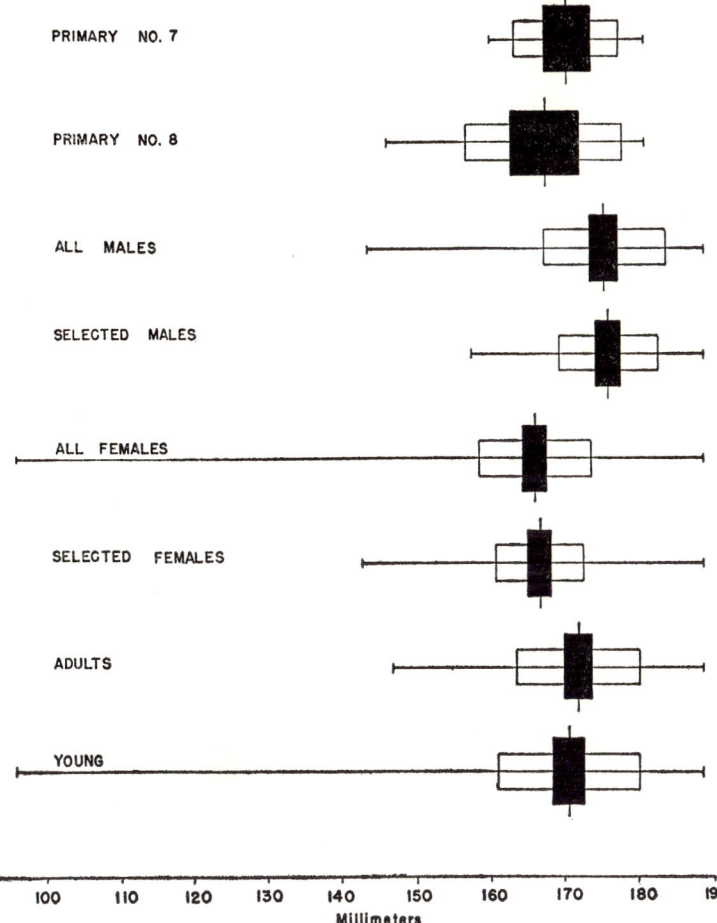

Fig. 11. Variation in the length of primary feathers of the greater prairie chicken by sex and age (*cf.* Table 2). The horizontal line indicates the range, the vertical line indicates the mean, the open rectangle indicates one standard deviation either side of the mean and the blackened rectangle indicates two standard errors either side of the mean.

Weights of the Greater Prairie Chicken in Autumn

Weights of 192 hunter-killed greater prairie chicken were obtained on October 24, 1951, by the use of spring balances. The balances were calibrated in 25 gram intervals. The weights were analyzed and presented in the same fashion as were the data on lengths of primaries. See table 3 and figure 12 on weight.

TABLE 3. WEIGHT CHARACTERISTICS OF THE GREATER PRAIRIE CHICKEN (CF. FIGURE 12). HEADINGS AS IN TABLE 2.

Sample	Extremes in Weights	$\overline{X} \pm 2 \frac{s_x}{n}$	s_x	V	n
Males	700-1100	951.20 ± 10.48	52.92	5.56	101
Females	650- 950	807.30 ± 11.38	54.25	6.72	91
Adults	750-1100	911.30 ± 16.12	81.70	9.00	103
Young	650-1050	853.00 ± 19.88	93.75	10.99	89
Old males	775-1100	975.40 ± 10.62	39.75	4.07	56
Young males	700-1025	926.40 ± 18.32	61.50	6.63	45
Old females	750- 950	834.90 ± 11.82	40.50	4.85	47
Young females	650- 875	777.90 ± 15.68	52.00	6.68	44

The average weight of the males, 951 grams, is significantly greater than that of the females, 807 grams, and the average weight of the adults, 911 grams, is significantly greater than that of the young, 853 grams. Furthermore, each sex- and age-class (old fe-

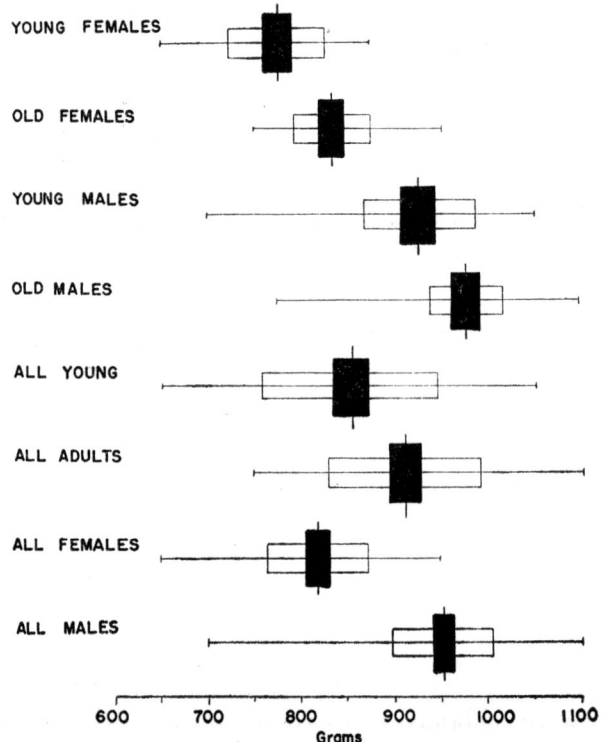

FIG. 12. Variation in the weight of the greater prairie chicken by sex and age (*cf.* Table 3). Diagrams prepared as for Figure 23.

males, old males, young females, and young males) has an average weight that is significantly different from that of each of the others, but there is a broad overlap between classes. The difference between the weights of birds of the year and birds more than one year old indicates that the young have not attained full size in late October. The low variability of both weights and lengths of primaries in young birds strengthens the conclusion that most of the young are hatched within a short period of time.

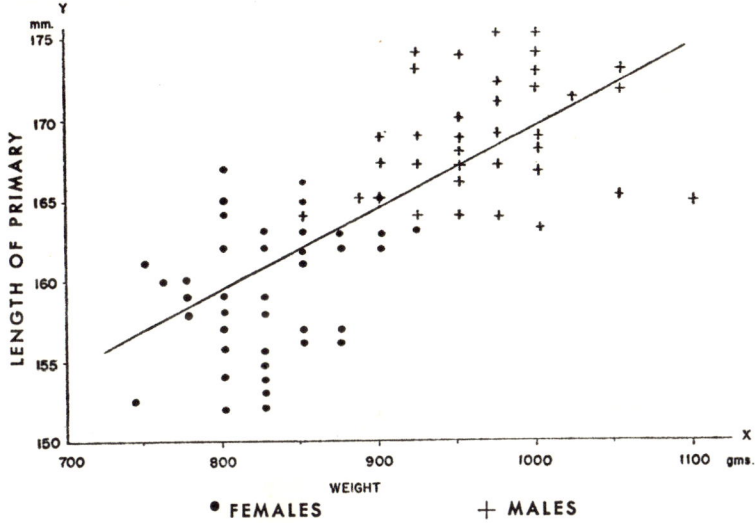

Fig. 13. Weight of adult greater prairie chicken (X axis) plotted against the length of primary number eight (Y axis) and the regression line of Y on X.

Figure 13 illustrates the correlation between the lengths of primaries and the weights of individuals in adult birds. This figure was prepared from the same data from adult birds that were used in the preparation of Tables 2 and 3 and Figures 11 and 12. Adult males could be distinguished from adult females in most instances if both the weights and lengths of primaries were known. The impossibility of obtaining such data from hunters on a mass basis makes the determination of sex impractical by this means.

Food Habits of the Greater Prairie Chicken

Studies of foods eaten by the greater prairie chicken show that cultivated grains make up an important part of its diet. Judd (1905) examined 71 stomachs from the Midwest and Canada, representing each month except July, and reported the following foods: insects 14.11 per cent, grain 31.06 per cent, flowers and shoots

25.09 per cent and fruits 11.79 per cent. The fruits were mostly rose hips, but included hazelnuts and the acorns of scarlet oak. Hamerstrom, Hopkins and Rinzel (1941:185) list cultivated grains, weed seeds and the browse of trees as the important foods in winter in Wisconsin. Schwartz (1945:72) found little evidence of the use of browse of trees in Missouri, but corn and sorghum were important winter foods. Yeatter (1943:414) reported ninety-one per cent plant food and nine per cent insects in summer in Illinois.

No reports, relating restrictedly to the Midwest, have been found listing foods used by prairie chickens prior to the growing of cultivated crops there, but the early writings of Audubon (1834:491-501) and Koch (1836:159) in reference to the prairie chicken in Kentucky and Missouri, respectively, list fruit, tree buds, grain, wild grapes, mistletoe, buds of willow and hazelnut, seeds of grass and flowers (presumably forbs generally), and the catkins and shoots of hazelnut. The German naturalist, Koch (*loc. cit.*), described conditions in the state of Missouri soon after it was settled, and mentions that the "cupido-huhn" moved from the prairies to the cultivated land along the Missouri River in autumn.

In the present study, information concerning foods and feeding habits of the greater prairie chicken was obtained by observing the birds in their feeding activities, by examining crop- and gizzard-contents and by studying droppings found in the Welda Area.

Crop- and gizzard-contents were washed, dried and analyzed by separating the food items and measuring the volume of each kind of food. Samples made up mostly of insects were preserved in alcohol and measured in a moist condition. Droppings were collected as entire deposits from a roost, and as such would contain remains of most, or all, of the foods eaten late in the previous day. Only fresh droppings were collected in order to make certain of the date of deposition. Droppings were washed free of urates and foreign material and then dried. The remains of the various food items were identified and an estimate was made of the percentage of each. The total volume of each sample was measured and the volume of each item was computed from the estimated percentage. This procedure is less exact than the analysis of crop- and gizzard-contents, but does yield a broad picture of the trends of feeding habits throughout the year that cannot be obtained otherwise, without sacrificing many birds. Sixty-five samples of droppings, 29 crops and 20 gizzards were analyzed.

In the droppings the remains of the more common seeds could be classified and insect material usually could be classified to family. Dicotyledonous leaves usually retained their shape, and the various cultivated legumes were readily identified. Leaves of grass seemingly were more thoroughly digested, but could be identified as such when found in droppings.

The greater prairie chicken ordinarily feeds early in the morning and late in the afternoon. In winter the usual behavior of the flock intensively studied near Welda was to fly to and from the feeding area, but some flocks were observed to walk to adjoining loafing cover from the feeding area. A female that was feeding on the leaves of weeds pulled off whole leaves approximately three inches long. Captive birds fed in similar fashion on lettuce leaves and swallowed in one piece leaves that were estimated to be 10 square inches in area. Whole seed-heads of crested plantain, *Plantago aristata* Michx., and parts of seed heads of sorghum with several seeds attached were found in crops. The manner of "browsing" is much like that of the turkey; the food is grasped and removed from the plant by an upward pull. Greater prairie chickens were never observed to scratch or otherwise attempt to uncover food on the ground, nor were they observed to browse in trees, although they were seen in trees in the winter of 1949-1950.

Habit, or an attachment to a known feeding area, seems to govern the selection of a feeding place. In the winter of 1950-1951, F-2 was used by 50-60 prairie chickens and a number of hogs and cattle. By spring, feed seemed to be gone, yet the birds continued feeding there while the same foods were abundant at F-1. The birds were observed to thresh soybeans from the pods at this time of scarcity. In the autumn, entire seed pods of soybeans were found in crops.

The data obtained from the analysis of crop- and gizzard-contents, from birds taken in the hunting season, are summarized in Table 4. The bulk (74 per cent) of the food was seeds and leaves of cultivated crops. Only 18 per cent was other plant material. Weed seeds (8 per cent) probably were used as much in October as in any other month.

Of the greater prairie chickens collected in July and August, 1951, three adults and five juveniles had food items in the crop or gizzard. Only a trace of insect remains was found in the adults, but in juveniles, insects made up approximately 25 per cent of the total volume of food, and occurred in each crop and gizzard that contained food. One individual had fed almost entirely on the larvae of a noctuid moth. The most important food item in summer, found in crops and gizzards of both adults and young, was oats; second in importance were the leaves of Korean lespedeza and other dicotyledonous plants. Seeds of four species of weeds were

TABLE 4. FOOD ITEMS FOUND IN 29 CROPS AND 20 GIZZARDS OF THE GREATER PRAIRIE CHICKEN TAKEN IN OCTOBER 1950 AND 1951, FROM ANDERSON, WOODSON AND COFFEY COUNTIES, KANSAS.

Food Item	Consumed	Per cent Occurrence	Per cent Volume
PLANT MATERIAL			
Monocotyledoneae			
Gramineae			
Panicum sp.	S	6.12	0.03
Avena sativa	S	6.12	1.58
Zea mays	S	24.49	14.87
Triticum aestivum	S	34.69	15.25
Sorgum vulgare	S	59.18	22.17
Unidentified	L	28.57	2.12
Cyperaceae			
Cyperus sp.	S	4.08	T
Dicotyledoneae			
Unidentified	L	36.73	6.43
Polygonaceae			
Polygonum sp.	S	18.36	0.02
Rosaceae			
Rosa sp.	S	22.45	0.92
Leguminosae			
Soya max	S	26.53	7.64
Lespedeza stipulacea	S	24.49	0.39
Lespedeza stipulacea	L	26.53	9.00
Strophostyles leiosperma	S	6.12	0.41
Strophostyles leiosperma	L	8.16	1.31
Trifolium repens	L	8.16	1.45
Medicago sativa	L	4.08	0.33
Oxalidaceae			
Oxalis sp.	S	2.04	T
Anacardeaceae			
Rhus sp.	S	2.04	1.63
Vitaceae			
Vitis sp.	S	2.04	0.10
Malvaceae			
Abutilon theophraste	S	2.04	T
Hibiscus trionum	S	28.57	2.16
Cornaceae			
Cornus paniculata	S	4.08	0.47
Acanthaceae			
Ruellia sp.	S	14.28	0.33
Rubiaceae			
Diodea teres	S	10.20	0.03
Caprifoliaceae			
Symphoricarpus orbiculatus	S	18.37	0.26
Compositae			
Ambrosia trifida	S	4.08	0.15
A. bidentata	S	8.16	1.14
Ambrosia sp.	S	34.69	0.96
Helianthus annuus	S	12.24	0.44
Plant debris		24.49	4.05
ANIMAL MATERIAL (Insects)			
Orthoptera			
Locustidae .... adults and nymphs		10.20	0.18

TABLE 4. CONCLUDED

Food Item	Consumed	Per cent Occurrence	Per cent Volume
Coleoptera			
Coccinellidae	adults	6.12	T
Hemiptera			
Pentatomidae	adults	6.12	T
Homoptera			
Cicadellidae	adults	18.36	0.13
Lepidoptera	larvae	2.04	T
Grit			4.05
SUMMARY:			
Total plant material (per cent of total volume)			95.64
Cultivated crop seeds		61.90	
Cultivated crop leaves		11.76	
Wild forb leaves		6.76	
Grass leaves		2.12	
Weed seeds		9.05	
Total insect material			0.31
Total grit			4.05

In the column headed "Part consumed," the letter "S" represents seeds and "L" represents leaves. Hard seeds such as those of *Rosa* and *Cornus* were found only in the gizzards and wear on seeds suggested that they functioned as grit.

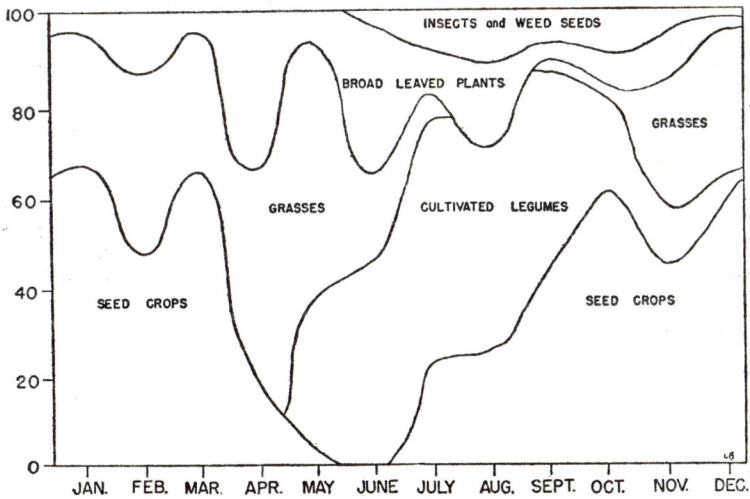

Fig. 14. Seasonal foods of the greater prairie chicken in Kansas. Cultivated grains are staple foods in winter and green foods are used extensively in winter.

found, but those of no one made up so much as one percent of the total volume of food and seeds of weeds obviously make up only a small part of the food under modern conditions.

[47]

All food items found to have been used by the greater prairie chicken are listed in Table 5. To ascertain the foods eaten, study was made of one or more crops or gizzards in each of the months of July through December and droppings were studied in each of the twelve months. The combined data on food are shown in Figure 14.

TABLE 5. MONTHLY OCCURRENCE OF FOOD ITEMS FOUND IN DROPPINGS, CROPS AND GIZZARDS.

Food item	Parts consumed	J	F	M	A	M	J	J	A	S	O	N	D
PLANT MATERIAL													
Gramineae	leaves	x	x	x	x	x	x	x	x	x	x	x	x
Panicum sp.	seeds							x			x		x
P. dichotomiflorum	seeds	x											
Avena sativa	seeds					x			x	x	x		
Zea mays	seeds	x	x	x	x	x				x	x	x	x
Sorgum vulgare	seeds	x	x	x	x						x	x	x
Triticum aestivum	seeds										x		x
Cyperaceae													
Cyperus sp.	seeds										x		
Scleria triglomerata	seeds						x						
Dicotyledonae (other than cultivated legumes)	leaves	x	x	x	x	x	x	x	x	x	x	x	x
Polygonaceae													
Polygonum sp.	seeds										x	x	
Rosaceae													
Rosa sp.	seeds									x	x		
Leguminosae													
Soya max	seeds	x			x	x	x				x	x	x
Lespedeza stipulacea	seeds										x		x
Lespedeza stipulacea	leaves				x		x	x	x	x	x	x	x
Trifolium repens	leaves						x			x	x		
Medicago sativa	leaves									x	x		
Oxalidaceae													
Oxalis sp.	seeds, pods									x			
Anacardiaceae													
Rhus sp.	seeds									x			
Vitaceae													
Vitis sp.	seeds									x			
Malvaceae													
Hibiscus trionum	seeds								x	x	x	x	x
Abutilon theophraste	seeds									x			
Cornaceae													
Cornus sp.	fruits									x	x		

TABLE 5. CONCLUDED.

Food item	Parts consumed	J	F	M	A	M	J	J	A	S	O	N	D
Acanthaceae													
Ruellia sp.	seeds, pods, calices										x		
Plantaginaceae													
Plantago aristata	seed heads					x							
Rubiaceae													
Diodea teres	seeds									x	x		x
Caprifoliaceae													
Symphoricarpus orbiculatus	seeds, berries										x	x	
Compositae													
Ambrosia trifida	seeds										x		
A. bidentata	seeds	x		x					x	x	x	x	x
Ambrosia sp.	seeds							x			x		
Helianthus annuus	seeds	x	x	x						x	x	x	x
ANIMAL MATERIAL													
(Insects)													
Phasmidae	entire							x	x				
Locustidae	entire							x			x		
Coleoptera (unidentified)	entire					x	x	x	x	x	x		
Chrysomelidae	entire							x	x				
Coccinellidae	entire								x				
Carabidae	entire									x			
Hemiptera													
(Pentatomidae)	entire							x	x				

[49]

In autumn, winter and spring, the greater prairie chicken frequently feeds on wheat. Much of the material found and identified as leaves of grass probably was wheat. In eastern Kansas 60 to 70 per cent of the food consumed by the greater prairie chicken is thought to be derived from cultivated crops, either seeds or leaves, whereas insects and weed seeds make up approximately 5 per cent and leaves of forbs and wild grasses make up the remainder.

At first inspection, these data might seem sufficient cause for condemning the greater prairie chicken as detrimental to agriculture. There is no doubt that the bird does consume large quantities of grain. Hamerstrom et al. (1941:193) found that penned birds of this species consumed, in addition to browse, approximately one and one-half ounces of grain per day per bird. This seems to be a fair estimate for wild birds, for a full crop contains more than one-half ounce of grain, and a bird would presumably eat more than two full crops of food per day. Accepting this figure as the average amount of grain consumed per day, a flock of 100 birds would consume approximately four and one-half bushels of grain each 30 days. In areas with flocks of 100 or more birds per square mile, as found in this study, it is obvious that a considerable quantity of grain would be consumed by them.

But, what is the source of this grain? Modern agriculture is based on the use of machinery. It is economical for the farmer to use machinery to harvest his crops, even though other methods might result in less waste. Formerly, when most grain crops were shocked and left in the field until threshed or fed, prairie chickens and other species made inroads upon this grain. In the Welda Area most crops were combined from the standing grain, or the shocks were removed from the fields before prairie chickens had begun to feed from them. An exception is that some oats remained in the shock during the wet weather of 1951. Mechanical harvest of crops in the field, leaves feed unavailable to cattle. This waste feed was the source of most of the grain used by prairie chickens in the Welda Area. At no time were the birds observed to use any grain other than waste. It is known, however, that damage to shocked grains occurs when the shocks are left in the field during the autumn and winter. This practice leaves the crop subject to loss from many granivorous forms of wildlife, and is not recommended.

The second large item of cultivated crops used by the greater prairie chicken is the leaves of legumes. The most commonly used cultivated legumes are those found in pastures—Korean lespedeza and white clover. Intensive feeding on newly sown alfalfa would probably be detrimental, but alfalfa was the least used of the cultivated legumes. Large numbers of greater prairie chickens do not occur in Kansas where less than two-thirds of the land is in native grass. Under such conditions, prairie chickens could hardly cause an appreciable loss of forage that was intended for cattle.

Fortunately, these facts are recognized by many farmers in areas where the greater prairie chicken occurs. These farmers recognize that much of the grain eaten by prairie chickens would otherwise be wasted. Even in 1949, when the population of the greater prairie chicken was high, few farmers interviewed complained of damage by it. Most farmers were interested in the welfare of the greater prairie chicken or at least tolerant of it.

There has been a tendency on the part of some authors to justify the presence of birds on the basis of the number of insects, detrimental to agriculture, consumed. This justification has had much to do with the widespread acceptance of birds as desirable. It is true that, in the aggregate, birds consume large quantities of insects. It is equally true that insects are adapted, by their reproductive capacity, to furnish this food for birds and other predators, without their numbers being unduly reduced. Lack (1951:443) points out that birds should not be regarded as harmful or beneficial unless the effects of birds on their food supply are known. In the light of present knowledge, it seems that we should regard any one species as a part of the integrated web of living things (the biota), and evaluate each species according to its net worth, whether this value be economic, esthetic or recreational. Viewed in this perspective, prairie chickens are eminently desirable, for they possess great esthetic appeal as part of a greatly diminished prairie biota, they provide a source of recreation for many hunters and are at least neutral in relation to agriculture as now practiced.

POPULATION CHANGES OF THE GREATER PRAIRIE CHICKEN

A preliminary report (Baker, 1952) summarizes a part of the information gathered in this study concerning population changes of the greater prairie chicken in Kansas. According to Stene (1946:9), prairie chickens were given protection by the first Kansas Legislature in 1861. This act, providing a closed season on prairie chickens, partridge and turkey, presumably reflected a depletion that had already occurred in the numbers of these birds. Common carriers were made liable for transporting illegal game in 1876.

The year 1903 marks the first time that an open season was not held throughout the State. The major points in the regulation of the hunting of prairie chickens in Kansas since 1903 are summarized as follows:

1903—season closed in some western counties and two eastern counties for the first time,
1913—season closed throughout the State for the first time,
1921—season reopened September 20 to September 30, daily limit of five,
1925—season closed,
1931—season reopened for two days,
1935—season closed,
1941—season reopened, one day, in six eastern counties,
1942—season opened, one day, in eight eastern counties,
1943—season opened, two days, in eight eastern counties, daily limit three, possession six,
1944—season closed,
1950—season reopened, one day, in fifteen eastern counties, limit two,
1951—season opened one day, in sixteen eastern counties, limit two,
1952—season opened one day, in eighteen eastern counties, limit two.

In 1943, few hunters succeeded in taking their limit, and many were completely unsuccessful. It may be inferred from this that a marked decrease in numbers of prairie chickens occurred in the period 1941-1943. At the beginning of this investigation, in 1949, the greater prairie chicken was again abundant, indicating a marked rise in numbers from 1943 to 1949. A conservative estimate is that there were 50,000 greater prairie chickens in Kansas in 1949.

Information concerning population changes of the greater prairie chicken was obtained in this study by repeated censuses of the Welda Area, particularly of one flock, and by interviewing hunters in the open seasons. Repeated counts of males using flock range A (see Figure 5) were made each fall and spring, and less frequent counts of the birds using flock range C were made. In each open season, birds were examined in the field to learn the sex and age of greater prairie chickens bagged, and hunters were interviewed to learn the number of birds killed and the length of time spent in hunting. In 1950, four investigators accompanied state game protectors and examined greater prairie chickens killed in six counties. In addition the writer concentrated his efforts in this respect in the Welda Area. In 1951, four two-man teams worked independently of the state game protectors in four counties characteristic of different types of habitat of the greater prairie chicken. In 1952, three two-man teams and two individuals working alone gathered similar data in six counties.

All greater prairie chickens examined were classified as young of the year, or as adults, by noting the condition of the two outer primaries (see Ammann, 1944). Sex was ascertained by examining the coloration of the rectrices, the pinnae and the air sacs (Ridgway and Friedmann, 1946:206).

The 1949-1952 Decline in Numbers

The changes in the population on the study area are presented in Table 6. These data represent the highest number of birds present in each flock for any one season in one day. No data were obtained from flock range C in the autumns of 1949, 1950 or 1951.

TABLE 6. NUMBER OF GREATER PRAIRIE CHICKENS USING TWO FLOCK RANGES ON THE WELDA AREA, 1949-1952..

Season and Year	Flock Range	
	A	C
Fall of 1949	146	?
Spring of 1950	104	43
Fall of 1950, before hunting	145	?
Fall of 1950, after hunting	72	?
Spring of 1951	47	31
Fall of 1951, before hunting	42	?
Fall of 1951, after hunting	24	?
Spring of 1952	15	15
Fall of 1952, before hunting	8	18
Fall of 1952, after hunting	6	12

Data on sex and age of greater prairie chickens examined in the two open seasons are presented in Table 7. Anderson and Woodson counties are representative of the best range of the greater prairie chicken in the Eastern Area. Chase, Chautauqua, Butler and Cowley counties are typical of the Bluestem Hills. The sample from Wabaunsee County was taken at the edge of the northern part of the Bluestem Hills and is representative of a condition intermediate between the Bluestem Hills and the Eastern Area. Data were obtained from 273 birds in 1950, 212 birds in 1951 and 119 birds in 1952.

Fluctuations of the population of greater prairie chickens in Kansas, prior to 1913, are not demonstrable, unless the action of the State Legislature in 1903 in closing some counties to hunting be taken to indicate a low point in numbers at that time. An all-time low seems to have been reached in 1913, when the season was closed throughout the State for the first time. A period of abundance in 1921 is reported by Clapp (1922:9). If open seasons indicate high populations, peaks of abundance occurred at the turn of each decade since 1920. Table 6 indicates that there was a marked reduction in the number of greater prairie chickens on the study area in the course of this study.

The reduction in numbers probably was not so great throughout the entire area open to hunting as it was in the Welda Area. It was estimated that in 1950 there were 30 to 35 hunters per square mile in the vicinity of Welda, and almost as many in 1951, but fewer in 1952. However, in adjacent Linn and Coffey counties in 1950, game protectors reported few hunters. Even in northern Anderson County, a more moderate decline in numbers is revealed by counts

TABLE 7. FREQUENCY OF OCCURRENCE OF SEX- AND AGE-CLASSES OF GREATER PRAIRIE CHICKENS EXAMINED IN 1950, 1951 AND 1952.

	Number of Prairie Chickens Examined											
County	1950				1951				1952			
	Males		Females		Males		Females		Males		Females	
	Young	Old	Young	Old	Young	Old	Young	Old	Young	Old	Young	Old
Allen.........	1	5	1	2	..	..	..	..	..	..	..	..
Anderson......	62	50	45	31	22	28	21	21	13	10	9	9
Butler.........	..	..	..	..	..	..	..	..	8	13	3	7
Chase.........	..	..	..	..	6	7	11	8	..	..	..	..
Chautauqua....	..	..	..	..	..	..	..	..	1	1	1	3
Coffey.........	0	1	1	1	..	..	..	..	..	..	..	..
Cowley.........	..	..	..	..	..	..	..	..	2	3	0	0
Greenwood.....	1	1	0	0	..	..	..	..	..	..	..	..
Wabaunsee.....	10	7	8	5	10	7	11	11	11	8	9	8
Woodson.......	12	11	11	7	9	16	7	17	..	..	..	..
Totals.....	86	75	66	46	47	58	50	57	35	35	22	27

of birds on booming grounds made in the spring of 1950 and in the spring of 1952. In 1950, there were 67 males on three booming grounds, and in 1952, there were 24 males on the same booming grounds. Even within and immediately adjacent to the Welda Area the effects of reduced hunting pressure were noted. The half-section pasture that was the principal range of flock C was closed to hunting in 1951. This flock suffered less loss than did the birds of flock A. Furthermore, in the quarter section immediately east of the area of study, hunting was prohibited in 1951, and the birds using this quarter section declined from approximately 75 in the spring of 1950 to 32 in the spring of 1952, as compared to the change from 104 to 15 in flock A in the same period of time.

Figure 15 shows the trends of the population of the greater prairie chicken in Missouri from 1920 through 1944, as given by Schwartz (1945:36), with the open seasons in Kansas superimposed by crosshatching. Also included is the hypothetical rise in the population of the greater prairie chickens in Kansas from 1943 to 1949 and the decline from 1949 through 1952 as indicated in the above discussion. Residents of the Welda Area say that the greater prairie chicken was nearly as numerous in 1948 as in 1949. Figure 15 reveals that the open seasons in Kansas have coincided roughly with the high populations of Missouri, but that at least the open season of 1941 fell somewhat after the peak population was attained in Missouri. Furthermore, the three consecutive open seasons, 1941-1943, were accompanied by a more pronounced decline than occurred in Missouri, without hunting, in the same period.

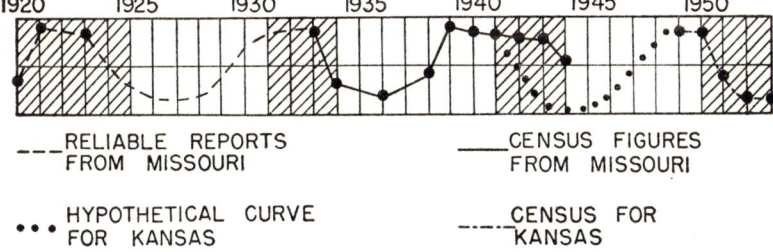

FIG. 15. Population trends of the greater prairie chicken in Missouri (after Schwartz, 1945). Open seasons in Kansas superimposed by crosshatching, the population curve from 1941 to 1949, inclusive, is estimated for the state of Kansas, and from 1949 to 1952, inclusive, is from the original data for the state of Kansas.

It should be emphasized that heavy natural losses of adult greater prairie chickens occurred in the period 1949-1952 in addition to the loss from hunting. Were this not true, the kill of approximately 50 per cent of the population each year, as indicated by the numbers recorded before and after hunting in Table 6, would have been balanced by the productivity of approximately 50 per cent, shown in Table 7, and the population would have remained more nearly static. It is evident, therefore, that the 1950, 1951 and 1952 hunting occurred in a period of naturally declining population, or at best a stable population and that the 1941-1943 open seasons probably occurred under similar conditions. It might be postulated that if open seasons were held in a period of increasing population, when production of young exceeds natural mortality, this population could sustain a greater kill by hunters without undue decimation. If this be true, a more efficient utilization of the prairie chicken as a resource could result, and high populations, which may elicit complaints from farmers and ranchers, could be avoided.

Changes in Age Composition

The age ratios, as revealed by the examination of birds killed by hunters (see Table 8), reflect the weather conditions of the three breeding seasons, and the average size of broods seen in 1950 and 1951 (cf. Figures 7 and 8). The productivity of the greater prairie chicken, as shown in Table 8, falls far short of that of the bobwhite (Bennitt, 1951:32), which experience has shown is a

TABLE 8. THE 0.9546 CONFIDENCE LIMITS OF CERTAIN POPULATION CHARACTERISTICS OF THE GREATER PRAIRIE CHICKEN, FROM BIRDS EXAMINED IN THE AUTUMN, 1950, 1951 AND 1952.

Sex and Age	Mean and Limits		
	1950	1951	1952
Per cent of females	0.412 ± 0.017	0.504 ± 0.068	0.414 ± 0.089
Per cent of young	0.556 ± 0.060	0.458 ± 0.068	0.480 ± 0.090
Per cent of females among young birds	0.436 ± 0.079	0.515 ± 0.144	0.393 ± 0.125
Per cent of females among old birds	0.384 ± 0.087	0.496 ± 0.159	0.439 ± 0.121

notably successful game bird. Yet the productivity of the greater prairie chicken found in my study is similar to that found by Lee (1950:476) for the lesser prairie chicken in New Mexico in 1949. If further study should reveal that 50 per cent is near normal productivity for the greater prairie chicken, this fact should be considered in its management. Under the conditions now existing in Kansas, no species with such a low productivity can withstand heavy hunting each year. The history of prairie chickens in Kansas indicates that their productivity, in view of their present limited geographic range, is not sufficient to provide annual moderately restricted hunting, for in each of the decades since 1920 open seasons have been held, and in each instance thereafter the population declined to so such a low point as to necessitate the closing of the hunting season for a number of years.

Changes in Sex Composition

Few data have been published relative to the sex ratios of prairie chickens. Schwartz (1945:14) calculated sex ratios from birds seen on booming grounds and found that only approximately 32 per cent of the population were females. Davison (1940:58) found a similar sex ratio in young of the lesser prairie chicken, and Lee (1950:477) found, in the same species, a preponderance of young males and old females in the bags of hunters in New Mexico.

The percentages of females, of the greater prairie chicken, killed by hunters in 1950, 1951 and 1952 in Kansas are given in Table 8. Of nineteen captive chicks, from the Welda Area, nine were of one sex and ten of the other, indicating a sex ratio at hatching of near 50:50. Significant departures from this ratio occurred among old females in 1950, but among young females the departure was not significant for the size of the sample, but it was suggestive of a differential mortality among young in favor of the males. The sex ratio did not depart significantly from 50:50 in the sample obtained in 1951 or 1952. It is not possible to say whether these differences are real or result by chance from sampling, but there seems to be but little doubt that, on the average, there are more males than females of the greater prairie chicken.

Differences in Abundance as Indicated by Hunters' Success

The success of hunters as an index to relative populations of game has been used in Missouri since 1947 (see Crawford, 1951:307). The method is theoretically sound, because the number of game animals bagged in a given length of time, on the average, should be related to the density of the population of game.

In each hunting season (1950, 1951 and 1952), hunters were interviewed to ascertain the number of birds killed and the time spent in hunting. The resulting data were computed in terms of birds killed per gun hour, and are presented in Table 9. The differences between each area sampled and between each year are highly significant statistically in most instances. To test the value of data on success of hunters we may first compare the results of the three hunting seasons in the Welda Area where populations were known. In 1950, hunters in the Welda Area killed, on the average, 0.376 birds per gun hour, and in 1951, 0.128 birds per gun hour. In 1952, too few birds were killed in the Welda Area to permit comparison. These data compare favorably with the populations of 145, 42 and 8 for 1950, 1951 and 1952 respectively

(Table 6). In other parts of Anderson County, populations probably did not decline so much in 1951 and 1952, and the hunting success was 0.214 birds per gun hour, 0.124 birds per gun hour and 0.059 birds per gun hour for 1950, 1951 and 1952 respectively.

A second test of the value of the success of hunters as a measure of relative populations may be made by comparing the data from Anderson and Woodson counties. The relatively poorer success in Woodson County, in 1951, may be correlated with the poorer productivity in that county, in 1951, as indicated by the low number of young birds bagged by hunters (see table 7). There were only 32.65 per cent of young in the sample from Woodson County, compared to 46.74 per cent in the sample from Anderson County. It is concluded that the average time required to bag a prairie chicken is a useful measure of relative densities of populations. On this basis, in the counties sampled, the greater prairie chicken

TABLE 9. THE MEAN NUMBER OF BIRDS PER GUN HOUR AND THE 0.9546 CONFIDENCE LIMITS OF THE MEANS, 1950, 1951 AND 1952.

County	Mean and Limits		
	1950	1951	1952
Anderson	0.214 ± 0.001	0.124 ± 0.002	0.059 ± 0.006
Wabaunsee	0.144 ± 0.016	0.134 ± 0.002	0.271 ± 0.024
Woodson	0.199 ± 0.008	0.092 ± 0.008	0.113 ± 0.014
Chase		0.082 ± 0.005	
Cowley, Chautauqua and Butler			0.164 ± 0.019
State wide average	0.185	0.109	0.109

is least numerous in Chase County, a part of the Bluestem Hills, and there were fewer birds in 1951 than in 1950 throughout the entire range in Kansas. Furthermore, the population in 1952, as indicated by hunters' success, made little recovery in spite of dry weather in the hatching season. The state-wide hunting success was the same for the two years (see Table 9). It is especially important to note that in areas of heavy hunting pressure, as in Anderson County, hunting success declined in 1952, whereas in less popular hunting areas (for example, Wabaunsee County), the success remained relatively good.

Management

Census

In general, census techniques have to be adapted to the peculiarities of the species censused. Most methods previously proposed for the census of prairie chickens have been based on their mating behavior. A census, adapted to conditions in Kansas, of prairie chickens on their booming grounds is recommended.

Two conditions found in Kansas should be recognized in outlining a census based on booming-ground counts. First, high winds frequently interfere seriously with the observer in the locating of booming grounds by the sense of sound. Experience has shown that this difficulty can be overcome, first, by limiting the census strip to one-half mile either side of the line of travel, second, by frequent stops and the use of binoculars, and third by being alert for birds to be seen against the horizon. Second, many continuous square miles of the Bluestem Hills and Blackjack Prairies are without county roads; in such roadless territory a system of census-plots should be used in place of census-strips. The procedure explained immediately below is modified from Schwartz (1945:31), and is recommended for censuses in spring.

1. Select adequate census areas to sample the entire range of both species of prairie chickens. In areas where roads form a regular grid pattern, census-strips one-half mile either side of a road should be selected. In roadless areas, census-plots of at least four square miles should be used as recommended by Davison (1940). Experience indicates that six miles of strip or four square miles of plot should be covered in one morning.

2. Preferably one census taker should be available for each county and should be assigned three or four census areas. In coun-

ties where prairie chickens are limited to only part of the county, proportionately fewer census areas could be assigned per county, and one observer might cover more than one county.

3. On one or more centrally located booming grounds the person in charge of the census should observe the progress of events until it is evident that the peak of mating activity is occurring. This is indicated by the presence of a fairly constant and high number of females appearing on the booming ground and usually occurs early in April. The census should be conducted in the week following the peak of mating. In the week of the census, the same booming ground should be observed to ascertain the number of females that are present on it each morning.

4. The actual census should be conducted for two hours in the morning beginning as soon as there is sufficient light to permit accurate observation. When possible, the counts should be made without flushing the birds and separate counts of males and females should be made. With a little experience, the census-taker readily can distinguish males from females by the more slender appearance and the attitude of indifference in the latter (Schwartz, 1944). Males ordinarily would be engaged in display, combat and pursuit activities, or might be squatting quietly at times when no females were present. With moderate to high winds, stops should be made each half mile on a roadside census, the surrounding terrain should be studied with the aid of binoculars, and any areas not visible from the road should be visited. When conditions for hearing are good, stops need be made at distances of only a mile, and visual survey of unseen parts of the census area is unnecessary. Complete coverage of each area is essential, or if an observer cannot cover the assigned areas, the part of each that was censused should be designated. Preliminary surveys of the census areas to locate booming grounds would facilitate the census, provided that the census was made only in the assigned week, and provided also that sole reliance was not placed on the booming grounds that were found in the preliminary survey.

5. All findings should be reported on standard forms to the person in charge of the census. The number of males per square mile would then be calculated. Total figures for the population of the entire state would not be necessary provided no major changes in the area occupied by prairie chickens occur.

Considering the potential losses, among young birds, caused by adverse weather, spring censuses are not sufficient bases for fixing regulations. Such counts would be most useful in ascertaining the trends of the population and the breeding stock present at the beginning of the breeding season. The 1951 and 1952 data relative to the spring and fall populations demonstrate that there was no net gain in numbers through the period of reproduction. It is imperative, therefore, to evaluate the success of reproduction each year in order to predict the fall population. A careful analysis of the amount and distribution of rainfall in the hatching period, May 15 to June 15, supplemented by counts of the number of birds seen in broods from July 1 to August 15, should be sufficient to supplement the spring census in predicting the fall population. If such a procedure were used over a period of years, a correlation between weather conditions and reproductive success probably could be established. If so, the counts of broods might no longer be necessary. Counts of broods might be obtained by field men incidental to their other duties; but early morning censuses with the aid of dogs probably would be necessary to obtain sufficient data. An accurate census of the fall population on the booming grounds could be made as early as the first or second week of October.

Hunting Regulations and Refuges

With adequate censuses it should be possible to set open seasons to harvest the surplus prairie chickens most efficiently. If seasons were opened when the census indicates that the population of prairie chickens is increasing and approaching peak numbers, full advantage could be taken of the favorable reproduction, and excessive abundance of prairie chickens could be avoided.

Judging by the effects of hunting in 1950, 1951 and 1952, more liberal regulations than those then applied cannot be permitted unless a much larger area is available for hunting, or unless there are fewer hunters. In the three seasons, in areas of high prairie chicken population, there were too many hunters. Too large a number of hunters placed excessive pressure on the prairie chickens, and also interfered with good sport.

Regulating the number of hunters by issuing limited numbers of special permits would be possible, and might eventually become necessary. A permit system could be used to gain also a better distribution of hunters. Under present circumstances the permit system is thought to be unnecessary, provided other measures are taken to insure the survival of a sufficient breeding stock.

One measure that should be seriously considered is to open the prairie chicken season at a time when the season is open on pheasants. This suggestion has been favorably received by landowners both in the pheasant country and in the prairie chicken country, for both are aware of an undue concentration of hunters. There is no way of predicting the net result of such a measure, but it could be expected that hunting pressure would be reduced for both species at least when the seasons were concurrent. A disadvantage for the manager would be the lesser number of enforcement personnel in any given area than there is now with the two seasons separated in time.

Sufficient protection probably could be given prairie chickens, with no limitation placed on the number of hunters, if a system of refuges were provided. It was pointed out in the section concerning population changes that small areas closed to hunting by landowners were effective in reducing the kill in 1951. It was observed, especially in 1951, that more areas were closed to hunting by landowners in areas where the numbers of the greater prairie chicken were small in Anderson County. In such areas, unsolicited posting of land probably will provide sufficient refuge areas. In areas of high population of prairie chickens, where farmers may desire a reduction in numbers, few refuges of this nature are likely to be provided. Yet, such areas have the greatest concentration of hunters, and are in the greatest need of refuges. Active promotion of a private refuge system in areas with high populations of prairie chickens, with the aim of providing a minimum of four square miles of refuge per township, should provide sufficient protection. Each refuge preferably should be one square mile or less in area.

In places where fires in the spring commonly remove nesting cover over large areas, refuge or management areas are needed to provide suitable nesting cover. Much could be done in this respect by encouraging ranchers not to burn their grasslands, and by offering assistance in the protection of their lands against fire. Many small areas, perhaps a total of 40 acres per square mile, would function better than a few large areas, since prairie chickens do not range far. Serious consideration should be given to the acquisition and management of refuge areas in the Bluestem Hills and Blackjack Prairie, where extensive burning is most common, and where land values are relatively low. State-owned refuges could serve as nesting and winter feeding areas, as demonstrations of proper grazing practices, and could be at least partly self sustaining by the lease of grazing rights. Special permits, similar to those used for quail hunting, could provide the funds necessary.

Range and Pasture Management

Prairie chickens are essentially birds of the grasslands. Fortunately, the practices recommended for the most profitable long-time use of grasslands are beneficial to prairie chickens. In much of the former range of the greater prairie chicken, however, where soils are adapted to the production of crops in rotation, the requirements of this species for permanent grass, probably can never be provided. In Kansas, the present acreage of native grassland is in little danger of reduction by plowing, for most of this land is unsuited to tillage. Every effort should be put forth, however, by agencies concerned with agriculture and conservation to protect existing grasslands, and to encourage the re-establishment of permanent grass, especially native grass, on areas proven unsuitable for cultivation.

Prairie chickens are benefited by moderate grazing of pastures. The paths and small areas of reduced cover resulting from the activities of cattle facilitate the movements of young birds, and provide places suitable for sunning in times when the grass is wet. Anderson (1946:95) recommends that grazing be deferred until four to six weeks after growth of grass begins in the spring, and that then the grass be grazed heavily for the remainder of the season. Under such a system, winter cover might be reduced by the heavy grazing, but spring burning would lose its appeal to the landowners, and nesting cover presumably would be more plentiful. Deferred grazing produces more pounds of beef per acre than early spring grazing and is well suited to the needs of the resident rancher who can provide supplementary pasture.

The usual practice is to begin grazing approximately on May first. This is especially true of pastures leased for the grazing of cattle from the Southwest, in which case the desire of the cattlemen is to attain the most rapid and early gain possible. Cattle may be taken from the pastures as early as July first, and the growth of grass thereafter is not only wasted, but it interferes with the efficient utilization of forage the next spring. The usual method of removing this unwanted growth is by burning. According to Anderson (1946:100) there is some justification for burning since it increases the efficiency of grazing by eliminating the old growth and because it permits earlier grazing. Burning is not recommended by Anderson, however, because the earlier grazing is detrimental to the grass, and the total production of grass is reduced. So long as absentee ownership and the leasing of pastures are prevalent, there seems to be no cure for the harm done to upland game by burning, except through a program of education and a system of refuges. Ranchers who insist on burning should be encouraged to do so only when the ground moisture is plentiful and after a rain. Under such conditions some cover is left.

Both deferred grazing without burning, and early spring grazing with burning have advantages for prairie chickens, but of the two, deferred grazing seems more desirable in that it provides improved conditions for nesting by the greater prairie chicken.

Restocking

In Kansas, all known large areas suitable for prairie chickens have at least a few birds present. In general, animals are capable, by natural increase, of stocking new range as rapidly as it becomes suited to them. If, in the future, areas that seem suitable for prairie chickens are not naturally stocked, by reason of their isolation, stocking could best be done by trapping and transplanting wild birds. Care should be taken to trap sufficient females, because experience has shown that they are more difficult to trap than are males.

SUMMARY AND RECOMMENDATIONS

1. Prairie chickens increased in numbers and extended their range with the development of early agriculture in the Midwest.

2. With the intensification of agriculture and with excessive hunting, the numbers and range of prairie chickens decreased.

3. Since the time of the first reliable estimates of the numbers of the greater prairie chicken, this species has fluctuated regularly in numbers. In Kansas, the declines have been accentuated by open seasons.

4. Kansas is one of the four states having the largest number of greater prairie chickens.

5. The greater prairie chicken in Kansas is confined to areas in which at least one-third of the land is in native grass, and is most abundant where approximately two-thirds of the land is in native grass.

6. The reproductive success of prairie chickens is low, because the reproductive period is short (late spring and early summer), and because adverse weather conditions may be detrimental to both eggs and young. The reproductive season seems to be the most critical period of the year for the species.

7. Weights of the greater prairie chicken and lengths of its primaries are both different according to sex and within each sex according to age, but neither weights nor lengths of primaries provide a sure means of distinguishing the sexes. Males average heavier than females.

8. Young of the greater prairie chicken can be aged by the condition of the molt.

9. In eastern Kansas, the greater prairie chicken feeds more on cultivated plants than on uncultivated plants. Of cultivated plant food eaten, most is waste that would not be harvested.

10. The success of hunters provides a means of comparing density of population in different years and in different areas in the same year.

11. A management plan is outlined for the greater prairie chicken, and is thought to be applicable to the lesser prairie chicken as well. The plan includes:

A. Censusing the adult population in the spring and in the fall to ascertain trends in numbers;

B. Censusing young birds between July 1 and August 15 to ascertain the success of reproduction;

C. Providing open seasons only in periods of increasing numbers, as indicated by the spring censuses, and in years of favorable reproduction, as indicated by the summer censuses;

D. Establishing refuges
> (1) One square mile in each township throughout the Blackjack Prairies and Bluestem Hills. Preferably state-owned.
> (2) One section in each nine sections in the eastern parts of the range where hunting pressure is excessive. Could be privately owned.

E. Encourage the preservation of existing prairies and the re-seeding to native grass of lands proven unsuitable for cultivation.

Literature Cited

AMMANN, GEORGE A.
    1944. Determining the age of pinnated and sharp-tailed grouses. Jour. Wildl. Mgt., 8(2):170-171, pl. 9.

ANDERSON, KLING L.
    1946. Range and pasture. Soil conservation in Kansas. Report of the Kansas State Board of Agriculture, LXV (271):92-117, figs. 51-67, table 15.

AUDUBON, JOHN JAMES.
    1834. Ornithological biography, Vol. II. Adam and Charles Black. Edinburgh, xxxii + 588 pp.

BAIRD, SPENCER F.
    1860. The birds of North America. J. B. Lippincott and Co., Philadelphia, lvi + 1005 pp.

BAKER, MAURICE F.
    1952. Population changes of the greater prairie chicken in Kansas. Trans. Seventeenth North Amer. Wildl. Conf., 359-366, 1 fig., 3 tables.

BENNITT, RUDOLF.
    1939. Some agricultural characteristics of the Missouri prairie chicken range. Trans. Fourth North American Wildl. Conf., 491-500, 1 fig. (plus one figure in text), 5 tables.
    1951. Some aspects of Missouri quail and quail hunting. Tech. Bull. Missouri Conservation Commission, No. 2:51, 2 figs., 34 tables.

BENT, A. C.
    1932. Life histories of North American gallinaceous birds (orders Galliformes and Columbiformes). Bull. U. S. Nat. Mus., 162:xi + 490 pp., 93 pls.

BUMP, GARDINER, ROBERT W. DARROW, FRANK C. EDMINSTER, and WALTER F. CRISSEY.
    1947. The ruffed grouse. New York State Conservation Department, The Holding Press, Inc., Buffalo, xxxvi + 915 pp., frontispiece plus 3 color plates, 144 half tone illustrations, 171 figs., 186 tables.

BUNKER, C. D.
    1913. The birds of Kansas. Kansas Univ. Sci. Bull., 7(5):137-158.

CLAPP, ALVA.
    1922. Sixth biennial report of the fish and game warden. State Printing Office, Topeka, Kansas, 22 pp.

COOKE, W. W.
    1900. Birds of Colorado, a second appendix to bulletin 37. Bull. State Agric. Coll., Agric. Exp. Stat., 56, Tech. Ser. 5:179-235.

COUES, ELLIOTT.
    1895. The expeditions of Zebulon Montgomery Pike. Vol. 2. Francis P. Harper, New York. 855 pp.

CRAWFORD, BILL T.
    1951. The field bag-check method of determining hunting success, pressure and game kill. Trans. Sixteenth North American Wildl. Conf., 307-314, 1 fig., 3 tables.

DAVISON, VERNE E.
    1940. An 8-year census of lesser prairie chickens. Jour. Wildl. Mgt., 4(1):55-62, 6 figs., 1 table.

DILL, HERBERT H., and WILLIAM H. THORNSBERRY.
    1950. A cannon-projected net trap for capturing waterfowl. Jour. Wildl. Mgt., 14(2):132-137, plate 4.

Duck, Lester G., and Jack B. Fletcher.
    1945? A survey of the game and furbearing animals of Oklahoma. Pittman-Robertson Series No. II, State Bull. No. 3, Oklahoma Game and Fish Commission, 144 pp., pls. I-LXVII, charts (figs.) I-XVI, maps I-XV, tables I-XXXIII.

Dwight, J.
    1900. The molt of North American Tetraonidae (quails, partridges and grouse). Auk, 17(1):34-51, (2):143-166, pls. iv and v.

Dyche, L. L.
    1912. First biennial report of the fish and game warden. State Printing Office, Topeka, Kansas, 35 pp.

Flora, Snowden D.
    1948. Climate of Kansas. Report of the Kansas State Board of Agric., LXVII (285):XII + 320, illus.

Fly, Claude L.
    1946. Natural agricultural resource areas of Kansas. Soil Conservation in Kansas, Report of the Kansas State Board of Agric., LXV (271): 126-195, figs. 76-126.

Goss, N. S.
    1891. History of the birds of Kansas. Geo. W. Crane and Co., Topeka, 692 pp., pls. 1-35.

Gross, A. O.
    1928. The heath hen. Mem. Boston Soc. Nat. Hist. 6:491-588, 12 pls.

Hamerstrom, F. N., Jr.
    1939. A study of Wisconsin prairie chicken and sharp-tailed grouse. Wilson Bull., 51(2):105-120, 2 figs., 9 tables.
    1942. Progress report No. 5, prairie grouse cooperative. Mimeographed.

Hamerstrom, F. N. Jr., and Frances Hamerstrom.
    1949. Daily and seasonal movements of Wisconsin prairie chickens. Auk, 66(4):313-337, pl. I, 2 figs., 6 tables.

Hamerstrom, F. N. Jr., Frank Hopkins and Anton J. Rinzell.
    1941. An experimental study of browse as a winter food of prairie chickens. Wilson Bull., 53(3):185-195, 2 figs.

Judd, Sylvester J.
    1905. The grouse of the United States and their economic value. Bull. U. S. D. A., Bureau of Biol. Surv., 24:1-55, pls. 1-2.

Koch, T.
    1836. Beobachtungen uber das cupido-huhn, *Tetrao cupido*. Archiv fur Naturgeschichte, 2:159-163.

Lack, David.
    1951. Population ecology in birds. Proceedings of the Xth International Ornithological Congress, pp. 409-448, Almquist and Wiksell, Upsala, Sweden.

Lee, Levon.
    1950. Kill analysis for the lesser prairie chicken in New Mexico, 1949. Jour. Wildl. Mgt., 14(4):475-477.

Lehmann, Valgene W.
    1941. Attwater's prairie chicken its life history and management. North American Fauna, 57:1-65, 14 pls., 4 figs.
    1946. Bobwhite quail reproduction in southwestern Texas. Jour. Wildl. Mgt., 10(2):111-123, pls. 8-9, 1 fig., 4 tables.

Long, W. S.
    1937. The birds of Kansas. Unpublished thesis, Univ. of Kansas, pp. 1-304.

McClanahan, Robert C.
   1940. Original and present breeding ranges of certain game birds in the United States. Wildlife Leaflet BS-158, U. S. D. I., Bureau of Biol. Surv., 21 pp., 35 unnumbered maps.
McDermott, John Francis (Editor).
   1940. Tixier's travels on the Osage Prairies. Univ. of Oklahoma Press, Norman, xv + 309 pp., illus.
Mohler, Levi L.
   1952. Fall and winter habits of prairie chickens in southwest Nebraska. Jour. Wildl. Mgt., 16(1):9-23, 2 figs.
Petrides, Geo., and Ralph B. Nestler.
   1943. Age determination in juvenal bob-white quail. American Midl. Nat., 30(3):774-782, 1 fig.
   1952. Further notes on age determination in juvenile bobwhite quails. Jour. Wildl. Mgt., 16(1):109-110.
Reardon, Jim D.
   1951. Identification of waterfowl nest predators. Jour. Wildl. Mgt., 15(4):386-395, 2 tables.
Ridgway, Robert, and Herbert Friedmann.
   1946. The birds of North and Middle America. Bull. U. S. Nat. Mus., 50, pt. X:xii + 484 pp., 28 figs.
Schwartz, Charles W.
   1944. The prairie chicken in Missouri. Conservation Commission, State of Missouri, Jefferson City. Approximately 178 pp., colored frontispiece + 84 unnumbered plates.
   1945. The ecology of the prairie chicken in Missouri. Univ. of Missouri Studies, 20(1):1-99, 32 photos, 12 figs., 8 maps, 26 tables.
Stanford, Jack A.
   1950. Missouri quail population surveys. Pittman-Robertson Quarterly, 10(1):50.
   1951. Bobwhite quail study. Pittman-Robertson Quarterly, 11(3):296.
Stene, Edwin O.
   1946. The development of wildlife conservation policies in Kansas. Gov. Res. Ser., Bur. of Gov. Res., Univ. of Kansas, No. 3, 38 pp., illus.
Stoddard, Herbert L.
   1931. The Bobwhite quail, its habits, preservation and increase. Chas. Scribner's Sons, New York. xxix + 559 pp., 69 pls., 32 figs., 49 tables.
Thwaites, Reuben Gold.
   1904-1906. Early American travels. Vols. 1-30, H. Clark and Co., Cleveland.
Westerskov, Kaj.
   1950. Methods for determining the age of game bird eggs. Jour. Wildl. Mgt., 14(1):56-67, 6 figs., 3 tables.
Yeatter, Ralph E.
   1943. The prairie chicken in Illinois. Bull. Illinois Nat. Hist. Surv., 22(4):377-416., 18 figs., 2 tables.

Transmitted January 26, 1953.